MIX-N-MATCH
LANGUAGE ARTS

AUTHOR
MIGUEL KAGAN

ART & DESIGN
ALEX CORE
CELSO RODRIGUEZ
MILES RICHEY
DENISE ALPHABET

EDITOR
KATHY TOMLINSON

PUBLISHER
KAGAN PUBLISHING

Kagan

Kagan Publishing

981 Calle Amanecer

San Clemente, CA 92673

(949) 545-6300

1 (800) 933-2667

www.KaganOnline.com

ISBN: 978-1-879097-70-4

TABLE OF CONTENTS

MIX MATCH

MIX-N-MATCH

INTRODUCTION

Transform content mastery into a fun and energizing learning game. Your students will enjoy mixing and quizzing each other so much, they won't even notice how much information they're learning. Mix-N-Match is a great class-building activity too. Students are out of their seats, having fun, and learning with all classmates.

HOW TO PLAY

On the following pages, you'll find step-by-step instructions. Here's a nutshell description of Mix-N-Match: Students each receive a Mix-N-Match card. They stand up and pair up. Students each quiz their partner, then get quizzed by their partner, then trade cards. They repeatedly quiz, quiz, and trade, each time with a new partner. Finally, the teacher has them find their partner with the matching card.

There are numerous additional learning games you can play with the Mix-N-Match cards in this book. We'll get to those in a few pages.

WHEN TO PLAY

The 12 Mix-N-Match sets in this book were designed to help students master basic information and skills. Pull out the corresponding Mix-N-Match set when you're studying a topic. The cards are great for acquiring the content and for review. If the content on the cards is new

content for your students, it is recommended that you introduce the content before they play.

One word of caution: Content mastery is important, but it's just one part of the entire educational picture. These sets were designed to supplement other great things you do in your classroom: the investigations, the projects, the discussions... They are not intended to replace them!

WHAT'S IN THIS BOOK

INTRO PAGE

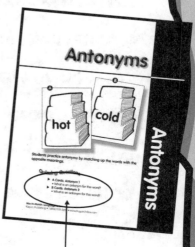

Each Mix-N-Match set has an intro page. On the intro page are "Quizzing Questions." These are questions you can have students ask each other as they quiz their partners using their cards.

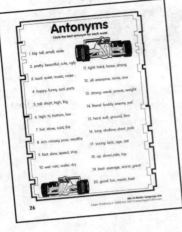

WORKSHEETS

Following the intro page, there are two reproducible worksheets associated with each Mix-N-Match set. These worksheets can be used to practice the concepts before playing Mix-N-Match or for reinforcing the concepts after Mix-N-Match.

You can use a variety of Kagan structures for the worksheets, or even have students work independently. We recommend you use the RallyCoach structure to have students do the problems on the worksheet. For RallyCoach, students pair up. Partner A solves the first problem while Partner B watches, checks, and praises or coaches. For the next problem, Partner B solves the problem while Partner A watches, checks, and praises or coaches. Partners take turns solving each problem. This structure allows students to watch how their peers solve problems and allows for peer tutoring when necessary.

MIX-N-MATCH CARDS

Next, and at the heart of the book are the Mix-N-Match Cards. On each two-page spread, you will find the matching cards so it is easy to see at a glance which cards are a "match." The card in the upper left corner on the even page matches the card in the upper left corner on the odd page.

ANSWER PAGE

On the last page of each card set, there is an answer page. On this page, you will either find the answers to all the matches in the card set, the answers to the worksheet, or additional helpful information for students. You can use these pages to check students' answers or when introducing or reviewing the matching content.

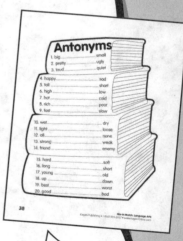

MIX-N-MATCH

Students mix, repeatedly quizzing new partners and trading cards. Afterward, they rush to find a partner with the card that matches theirs.

Mix-N-Match
Kagan Publishing • 1 (800) 933-2667 • www.KaganOnline.com

SET-UP

Copy a Mix-N-Match card set for your class. Cut out the cards, or have students cut out the cards. Distribute the cards so each students receives one card.

S T E P S

1 STUDENTS STANDUP—HANDUP—PAIRUP
With a card in their hands, students stand up, push in their chairs, and put their hands up. They keep a hand up until they find a partner. Students use the card to quiz their partners. For example, for the Antonyms set, one student with an antonym card asks, "What's an antonym for my word?"

2 STUDENTS QUIZ PARTNERS
The partner answers. If correct, the partner receives a compliment ("Excellent job!" "Great work!"), or a high five. If incorrect or no answer is given, the partner is given the answer and coached how to remember it.

3 SWITCH ROLES: STUDENTS QUIZ PARTNERS
The other partner quizzes, then praises or coaches. For example, the student with other antonym card asks, "What's an antonym for my word?"

4 PARTNERS TRADE CARDS
Partners trade cards and say, "thank you," or "good-bye."

5 REPEAT WITH NEW PARTNERS
Partners split up and repeat Steps 1 through 4 a number of times, repeatedly quizzing new partners and being quizzed by new partners.

6 TEACHER CALLS "FREEZE"
After numerous pairings and ample quizzing time, call, "freeze."

7 STUDENTS FREEZE
Students freeze, look at their cards, and think of their match.

8 STUDENTS FIND THEIR MATCH
Students move to the center of the room, find their match, and quickly move away from the center of the room with their new partner.

EXTENSION

Once students are around the room in pairs, have them each quickly share their match. For our example, one student would say, "An antonym for hot is...," and his or her partner chimes in, "cold."

QUIZ-QUIZ-TRADE

MANAGEMENT TIPS

COLOR CODE CARDS

Copy the cards onto two different color card stock papers. Use one color for the cards on even page numbers, and a different color for the cards on odd page numbers. This way, you can easily tell the cards apart.

LAMINATE CARDS

Laminate your card sets to make them more attractive and last for years.

COLLECTING CARDS

When you collect the cards from your students, have them return them in pairs. This will save you lots of time: you get the cards back ready to use the next time.

STORE SETS

Put your card set into an envelope for next time. Each set has a title bar that you cut off when you cut out the cards. Tape that title to the front of your envelope. Or store sets using a rubber band or binder clip.

CARD PAIRS

Each card has a matching card. When distributing the cards, make sure you distribute them in pairs. If you have an extra student, you can either have that student be a "twin" with another student, or you can join in.

MORE STUDENTS THAN CARDS

Card sets are designed for up to 40 students. If you have more than 40 students, make extra copies of the card pairs you'd most like to have students work on. This way, each student gets a card and students practice the desired content more frequently.

PARTIAL SET

If students are having difficulty with specific matching cards, make multiple copies of those cards and have students play Mix-N-Match with this partial set for repeated practice. A partial set is also helpful if there are some cards beyond students' ability level.

Antonyms

HAND UP

Have students put their hands up as soon as they're ready to find a new partner, and put them down as soon as they've found a partner. This makes it easy for students to find partners. If you see a student avoiding another student with his/her hand up, stop the class and remind them to always pair with the nearest person with a hand up.

HIGH FIVE

Students have their hands up when searching for a partner. Have students give each other a high five, then greet each other with a handshake or a friendly greeting ("Hey, buddy") before they quiz each other. This adds to the excitement of the game.

EXAGGERATED PRAISERS

Another thing you can do spice up Mix-N-Match is use exaggerated praisers. Have students use funny compliments that are a little overboard but make us feel good, nevertheless. For example, "That's correct. You must have been awarded at least a dozen Nobel prizes."

NO REPEATS

Tell students that they cannot pair up with the same partner twice.

NOBODY KNOWS

If neither partner knows the answer to a card, have them write it down on a designated area of the chalkboard. The resulting list is a great way to see which cards students need more work on.

MAKE IT A RACE

Record how long it takes students to find their matching partners. Do it repeatedly and see if students can get quicker and beat their previous times.

MAKE YOUR OWN SETS

This book contains 12 ready-to-use sets based on popular topics. It'll provide hours of fun and learning. If you'd like more sets, you can easily create your own Mix-N-Match sets. All you need is matching content. Problems and answers work well. Words and their definitions are also popular.

MORE STRUCTURES

The card sets in this book were designed for Mix-N-Match.
But you can also use them with a number of other Kagan Structures...

NUMBERED HEADS TOGETHER

In teams, students number off. Select a card and ask students a question based on the content of the card. Have each student independently write his/her own answer on a sheet of paper or response board. Then, students put their heads together to make sure everyone on their team knows the answer. Call a number and have students with that number share their team's answer.

FLASHCARD GAME

Flashcard Game is based on repeated practice and proceeds through three rounds from the most cues to the least.

Students have a stack of cards they need to practice and a list of correct answers. The student (the tutee) gives his/her cards and answers to a partner (the tutor). The tutor shows the tutee the card and reads the answer. Next, the tutor shows the tutee the card and the tutee answers. If correct, the tutee wins the card back. If wrong, the tutor gives the tutee the correct answer and returns the card to the stack. Once the tutee wins all his/her cards, they proceed to Round 2. In Round 2, the tutor shows the tutee the card and the tutee answers. Once the tutee wins all his/her cards in Round 2, the pair proceeds to Round 3. In Round 3, the tutor does not show the card. He or she reads the card and the tutee answers.

Mix-N-Match
Kagan Publishing • 1 (800) 933-2667 • www.KaganOnline.com

SHOWDOWN

In teams, students place a deck of cards face down in the center of the team table. One student turns over the first card. All students independently write the answer on a sheet of paper or on a slate. When all students indicate they're ready, a student calls, "showdown" and they all show their answers. If correct, they celebrate. If not, teammates coach, then celebrate.

RALLYTABLE

In pairs, students place a stack of cards between them. Student A turns over the first card and states the "match." Student B turns over the next card and states the match. Students take turns, stating the match for each new card.

ROUNDTABLE

In teams, students place a stack of cards between them. Each student takes a turn turning over the top card and stating the "match." The game continues until the team has gone through all the cards.

SOLO

Give a student a deck of cards. The student shuffles the cards, then makes matching card pairs.

CONCENTRATION

Concentration can be played as a pair or as a small group. Students shuffle the cards and place them face down in a grid pattern (see below) without looking at the cards. The first student turns over two cards. If they match, he/she wins that pair and gets another turn. If he/she does not make a pair, he/she returns the cards to their original place, face down. The next student takes a turn. When there are no more cards left to turn over, students count the cards they won and congratulate the student with the most cards.

LET'S PLAY!

Abbreviations

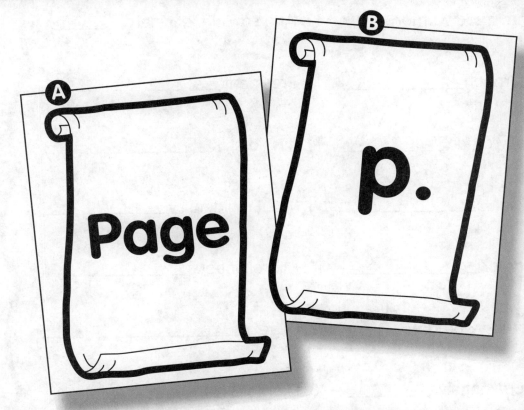

Students practice abbreviations by matching words or phrases with their abbreviations.

Quizzing Questions

▶ **A Cards: Words or Phrases**
  • What is my abbreviation?
▶ **B Cards: Abbreviations**
  • What am I an abbreviation for?

Abbreviations

Abbreviations

Write the abbreviation of the word or phrase on the line provided.

1. Before noon _____

2. Unmarried woman _____

3. Afternoon _____

4. Any woman _____

5. Mister _____

6. Senator _____

7. Married woman _____

8. Representative _____

9. Honorable (judge) _____

10. Continued _____

11. Governor _____

12. And so forth (et cetera) _____

13. President _____

14. It is (id est) _____

15. Vice President _____

16. Miscellaneous _____

17. Page _____

18. Example _____

19. Pages _____

20. Volume _____

Mix-N-Match: Language Arts
Kagan Publishing • 1 (800) 933-2667 • www.KaganOnline.com

Abbreviations

Write the meaning of the abbreviation on the line provided.

1. A.M. or a.m._____

2. Miss_____

3. P.M. or p.m._____

4. Ms._____

5. Mr._____

6. Sen._____

7. Mrs._____

8. Rep._____

9. Hon._____

10. cont._____

11. Gov._____

12. etc._____

13. Pres._____

14. i.e._____

15. V.P._____

16. misc._____

17. p._____

18. ex. or Ex._____

19. pp_____

20. vol._____

Abbreviations

Before noon

Unmarried woman

Afternoon

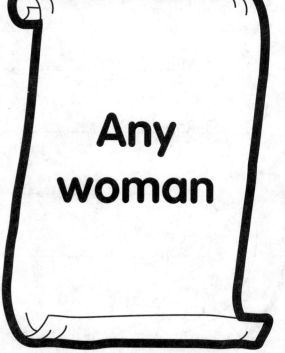

Any woman

Mix-N-Match: Language Arts
Kagan Publishing • 1 (800) 933-2667 • www.KaganOnline.com

Abbreviations

A.M.
or a.m.

Abbreviations © Kagan Publishing

Miss

Abbreviations © Kagan Publishing

P.M. or
p.m.

Abbreviations © Kagan Publishing

Ms.

Abbreviations © Kagan Publishing

Abbreviations

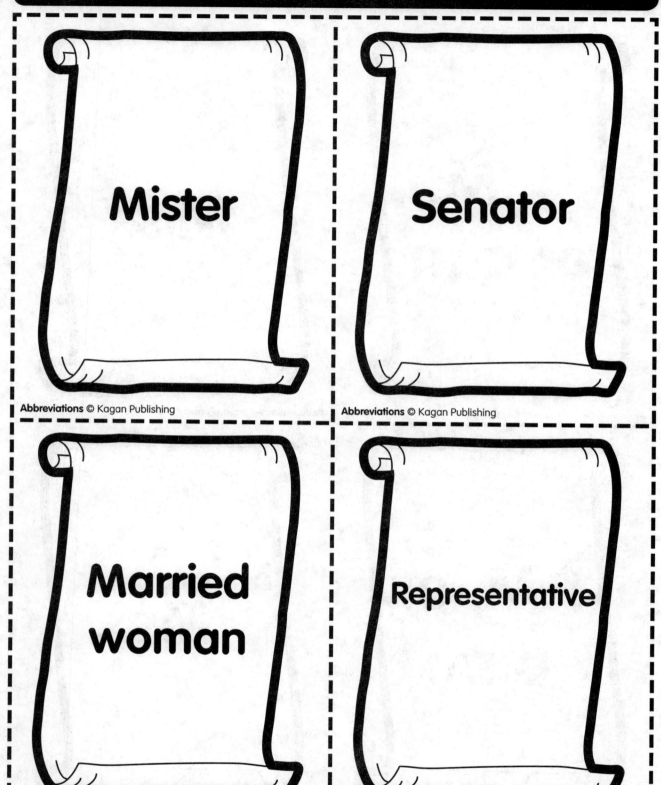

Mister

Senator

Married woman

Representative

Mix-N-Match: Language Arts
Kagan Publishing • 1 (800) 933-2667 • www.KaganOnline.com

Abbreviations

Mr.

Sen.

Mrs.

Rep.

Abbreviations © Kagan Publishing

Abbreviations © Kagan Publishing

Abbreviations © Kagan Publishing

Abbreviations © Kagan Publishing

Abbreviations

Honorable (Judge)

Continued

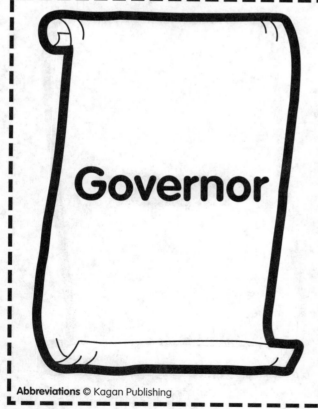

Governor

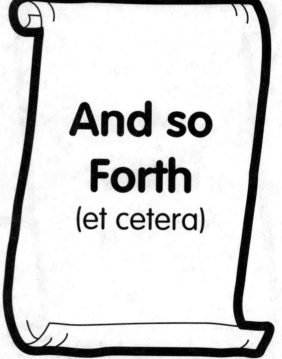

And so Forth (et cetera)

Hon.

Cont.

Gov.

etc.

Abbreviations

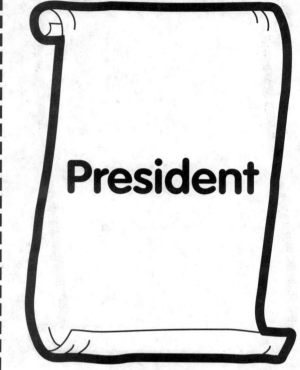

President

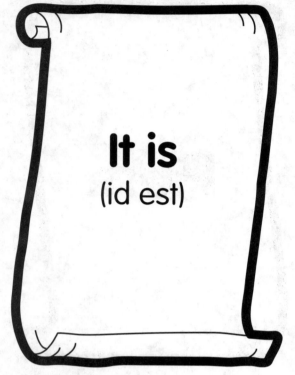

It is
(id est)

Vice President

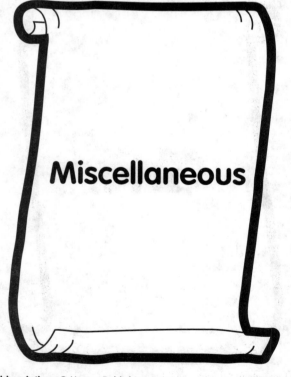

Miscellaneous

Abbreviations

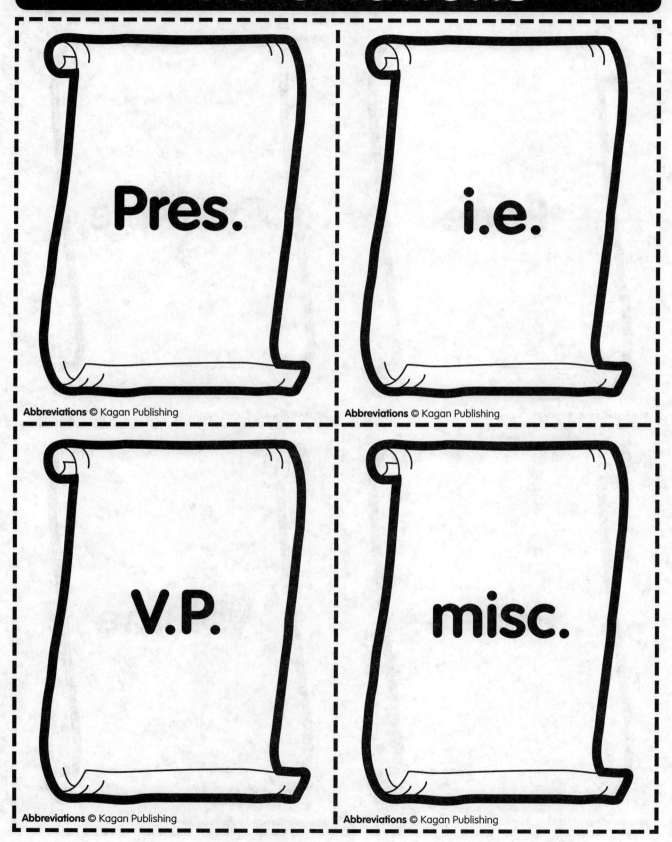

Pres.

i.e.

Abbreviations © Kagan Publishing

Abbreviations © Kagan Publishing

V.P.

misc.

Abbreviations © Kagan Publishing

Abbreviations © Kagan Publishing

Abbreviations

Page

Example

Abbreviations © Kagan Publishing

Abbreviations © Kagan Publishing

Pages

Volume

Abbreviations © Kagan Publishing

Abbreviations © Kagan Publishing

Kagan Publishing • 1 (800) 933-2667 • www.KaganOnline.com

Abbreviations

p.

ex. or
Ex.

Abbreviations © Kagan Publishing

Abbreviations © Kagan Publishing

pp.

vol.

Abbreviations © Kagan Publishing

Abbreviations © Kagan Publishing

Abbreviations

1. Before noon ....................A.M. or a.m.
2. Unmarried woman ....Miss
3. Afternoon ....................P.M. or p.m.
4. Any woman ....Ms.
5. Mister ....Mr.
6. Senator .... Sen.
7. Married woman...............Mrs.
8. Representative ....Rep.
9. Honorable (judge)............Hon.
10. Continued.........................cont.
11. Governor ....Gov.
12. And so forth (et cetera).......etc.
13. President...........................Pres.
14. It is (id est)..........................i.e.
15. Vice President ....................V.P.
16. Miscellaneous ....misc.
17. Page .... p.
18. Example ....ex. or Ex.
19. Pages ....pp.
20. Volume...............................vol.

Mix-N-Match: Language Arts
Kagan Publishing • 1 (800) 933-2667 • www.KaganOnline.com

Antonyms

Students practice antonyms by matching up the words with the opposite meanings.

Quizzing Questions

▶ **A Cards: Antonym 1**
  • What is an antonym for this word?
▶ **B Cards: Antonym 2**
  • What is an antonym for this word?

Mix-N-Match: Language Arts
Kagan Publishing • 1 (800) 933-2667 • www.KaganOnline.com

Antonyms

Circle the best antonym for each word.

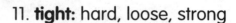

1. **big:** tall, small, wide

2. **pretty:** beautiful, cute, ugly

3. **loud:** quiet, music, noise

4. **happy:** funny, sad, party

5. **tall:** short, high, big

6. **high:** hi, bottom, low

7. **hot:** stove, cold, fire

8. **rich:** money, poor, wealthy

9. **fast:** slow, speed, stop

10. **wet:** rain, water, dry

11. **tight:** hard, loose, strong

12. **all:** everyone, none, one

13. **strong:** weak, power, weight

14. **friend:** buddy, enemy, pal

15. **hard:** soft, ground, firm

16. **long:** shallow, short, pole

17. **young:** kids, age, old

18. **up:** down, side, top

19. **best:** average, worst, great

20. **good:** fun, mean, bad

26

Antonym Crossword

Fill in the crossword using the antonym of the word.

Antonyms

Answers

Across
1. sad
2. poor
3. small
4. none
5. dry
6. loose
7. soft
8. bad
15. down
16. cold

Down
1. low
3. worst
9. short
10. old
11. slow
12. ugly
13. enemy
14. weak
17. tall
18. quiet

Teacher Note
Cover up answers before duplicating.

Antonyms

big

Antonyms © Kagan Publishing

pretty

Antonyms © Kagan Publishing

loud

Antonyms © Kagan Publishing

happy

Antonyms © Kagan Publishing

Mix-N-Match: Language Arts
Kagan Publishing • 1 (800) 933-2667 • www.KaganOnline.com

Antonyms

small

Antonyms © Kagan Publishing

ugly

Antonyms © Kagan Publishing

quiet

Antonyms © Kagan Publishing

sad

Antonyms © Kagan Publishing

Antonyms

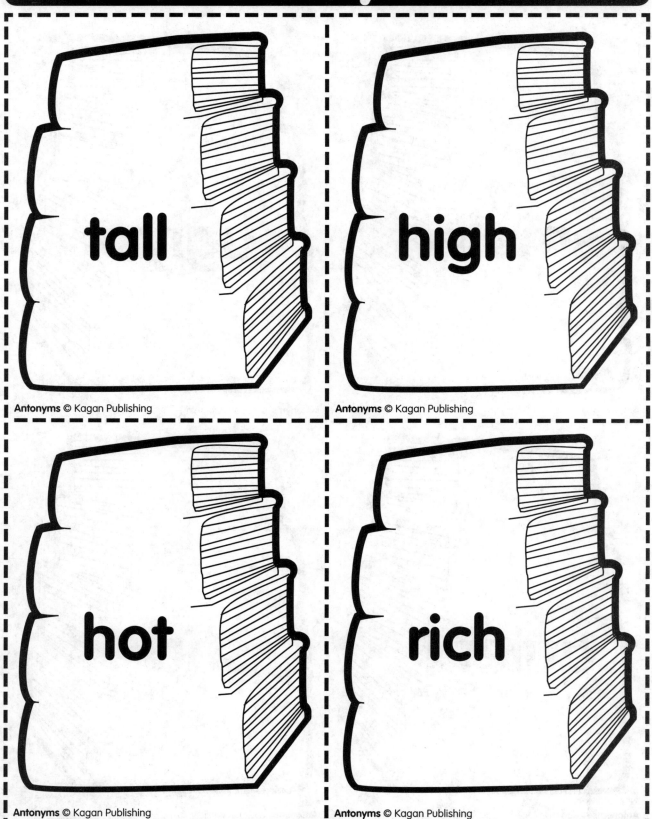

tall

Antonyms © Kagan Publishing

high

Antonyms © Kagan Publishing

hot

Antonyms © Kagan Publishing

rich

Antonyms © Kagan Publishing

Antonyms

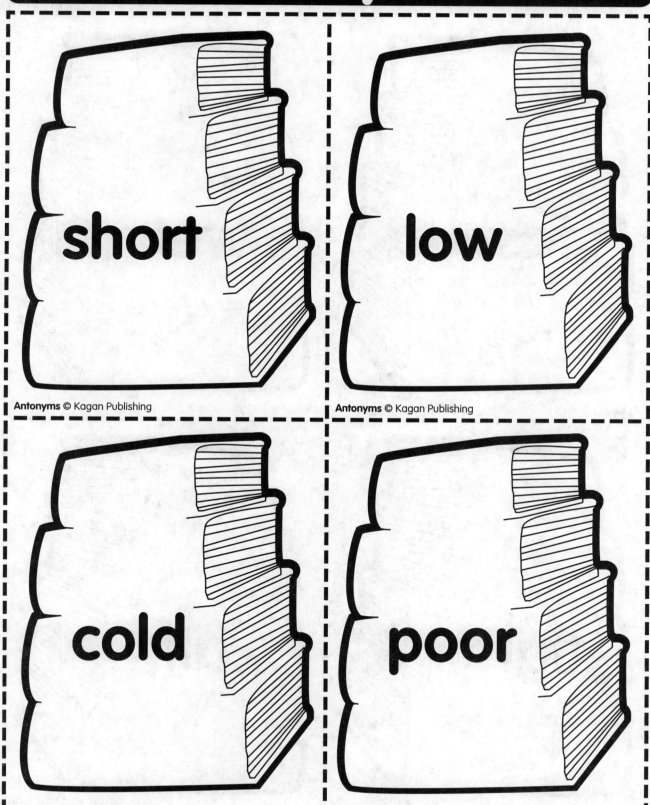

short

Antonyms © Kagan Publishing

low

Antonyms © Kagan Publishing

cold

Antonyms © Kagan Publishing

poor

Antonyms © Kagan Publishing

Antonyms

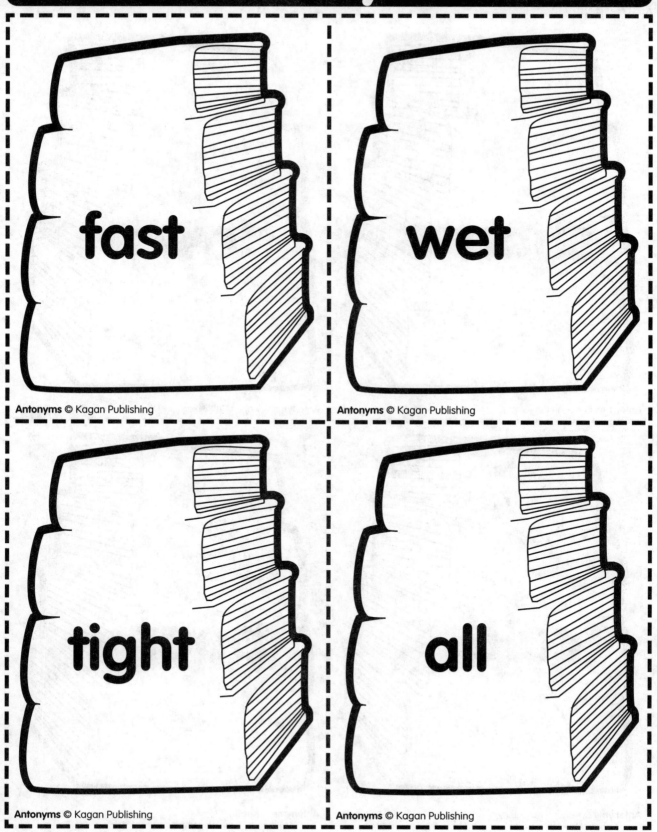

fast

wet

tight

all

Antonyms © Kagan Publishing

Antonyms © Kagan Publishing

Antonyms © Kagan Publishing

Antonyms © Kagan Publishing

Antonyms

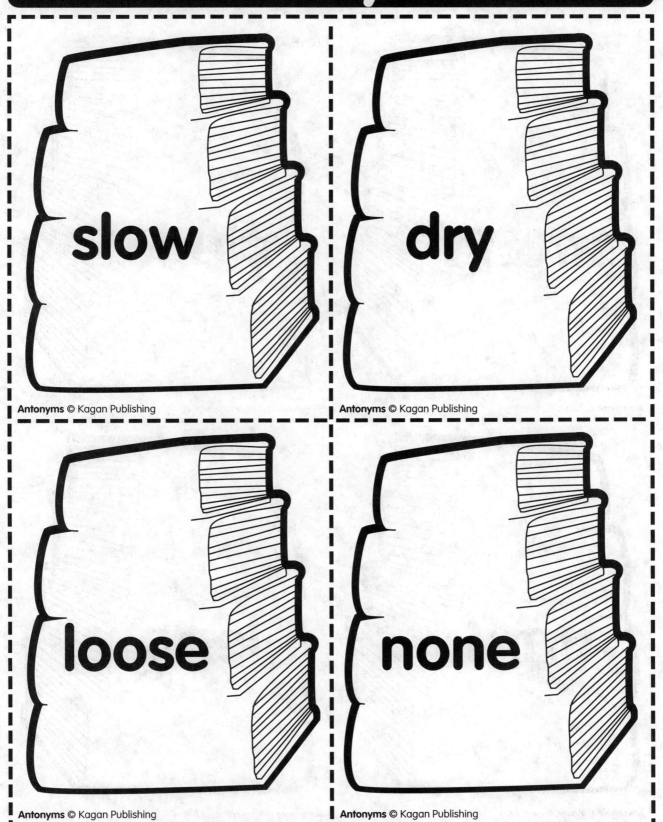

slow

Antonyms © Kagan Publishing

dry

Antonyms © Kagan Publishing

loose

Antonyms © Kagan Publishing

Antonyms © Kagan Publishing

Antonyms

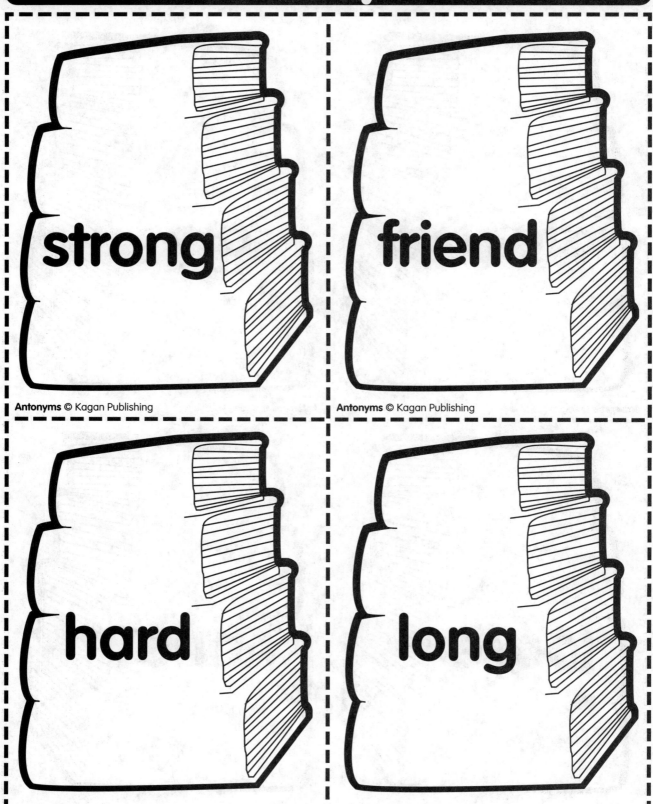

strong

Antonyms © Kagan Publishing

friend

Antonyms © Kagan Publishing

hard

Antonyms © Kagan Publishing

long

Antonyms © Kagan Publishing

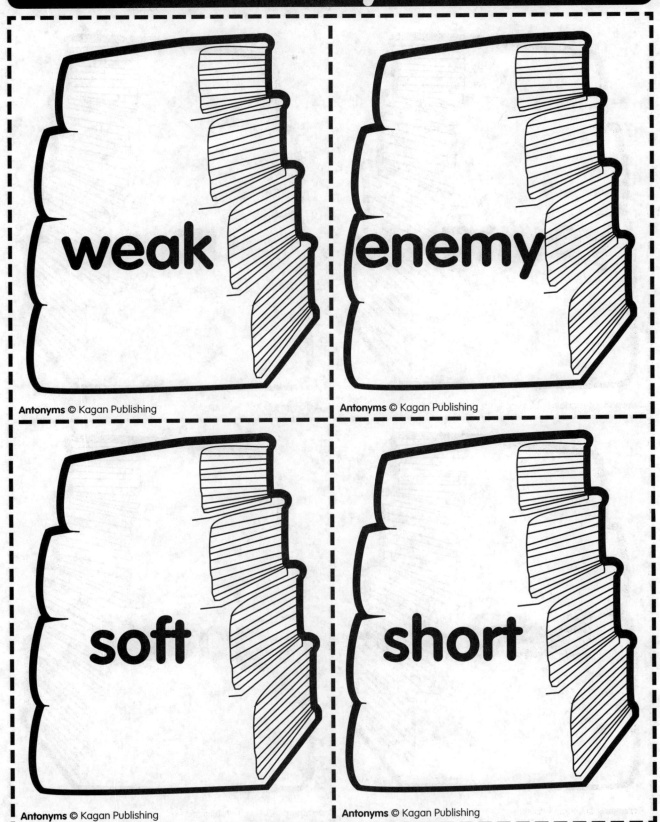

weak

Antonyms © Kagan Publishing

enemy

Antonyms © Kagan Publishing

soft

Antonyms © Kagan Publishing

short

Antonyms © Kagan Publishing

young

up

best

good

Mix-N-Match: Language Arts
Kagan Publishing • 1 (800) 933-2667 • www.KaganOnline.com

Antonyms

old

Antonyms © Kagan Publishing

down

Antonyms © Kagan Publishing

worst

Antonyms © Kagan Publishing

bad

Antonyms © Kagan Publishing

Antonyms

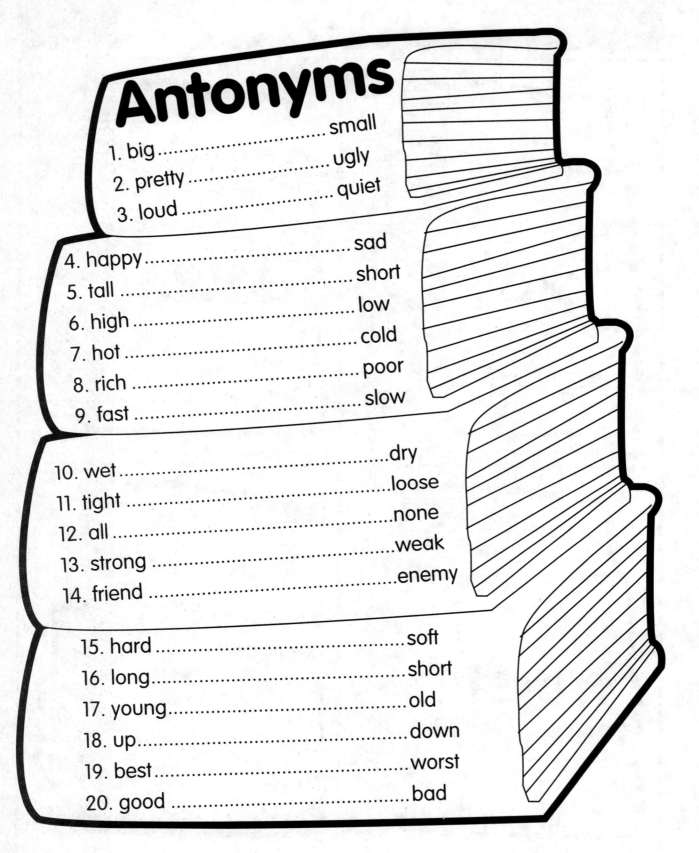

1. big .... small
2. pretty .... ugly
3. loud .... quiet

4. happy .... sad
5. tall .... short
6. high .... low
7. hot .... cold
8. rich .... poor
9. fast .... slow

10. wet .... dry
11. tight .... loose
12. all .... none
13. strong .... weak
14. friend .... enemy

15. hard .... soft
16. long .... short
17. young .... old
18. up .... down
19. best .... worst
20. good .... bad

Mix-N-Match: Language Arts
Kagan Publishing • 1 (800) 933-2667 • www.KaganOnline.com

Classifying Nouns

A School

B Place

Students practice classifying nouns by determining if the noun is either a person, place, or thing.

Quizzing Questions

▶ **A Cards: Nouns**
  • Am I a person, place, or thing?
▶ **B Cards: Person, Place, or Thing**
  • Name a person, place, or thing.

Classifying Nouns

In the line provided, write whether the noun is a person, place, or thing.

1._____

2._____

3._____

4._____

5._____

6._____

7._____

8._____

9._____

Mix-N-Match: Language Arts
Kagan Publishing • 1 (800) 933-2667 • www.KaganOnline.com

Classifying Nouns

Write five examples for each a person, place, or thing.

Person

1. _____
2. _____
3. _____
4. _____
5. _____

Place

1. _____
2. _____
3. _____
4. _____
5. _____

Thing

1. _____
2. _____
3. _____
4. _____
5. _____

Classifying Nouns

Brother

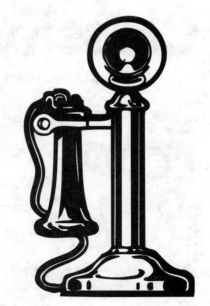

Telephone

Ball

Dad

Mix-N-Match: Language Arts
Kagan Publishing • 1 (800) 933-2667 • www.KaganOnline.com

Classifying Nouns

Person

Thing

Classifying Nouns © Kagan Publishing

Classifying Nouns © Kagan Publishing

Thing

Person

Classifying Nouns © Kagan Publishing

Classifying Nouns © Kagan Publishing

Classifying Nouns

Beach

Computer

Niece

Park

Classifying Nouns

Place

Thing

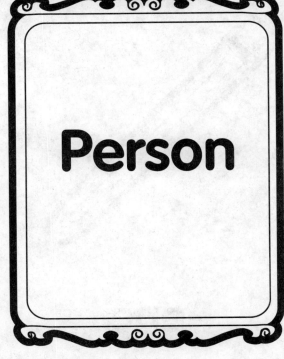

Person

Place

Classifying Nouns

Book

Mother

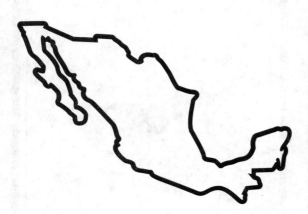

Mexico

Pencil

Mix-N-Match: Language Arts
Kagan Publishing • 1 (800) 933-2667 • www.KaganOnline.com

Classifying Nouns

Thing

Person

Classifying Nouns © Kagan Publishing

Classifying Nouns © Kagan Publishing

Place

Thing

Classifying Nouns © Kagan Publishing

Classifying Nouns © Kagan Publishing

Classifying Nouns

Mayor

River

Trash Can

Actor

Classifying Nouns

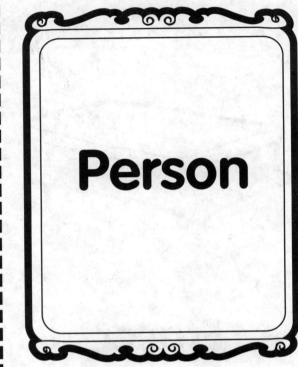

Person

Place

Thing

Person

Classifying Nouns

School

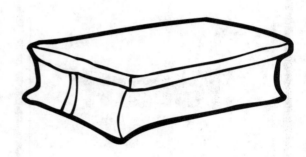

Eraser

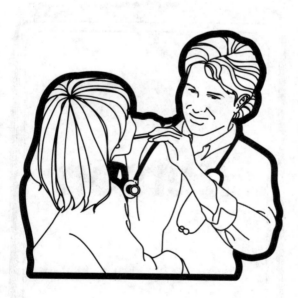

Doctor

Church

Mix-N-Match: Language Arts
Kagan Publishing • 1 (800) 933-2667 • www.KaganOnline.com

Classifying Nouns

Place

Thing

Person

Place

Classifying Nouns

Person

- Brother
- Dad
- Niece
- Mother
- Mayor
- Actor
- Doctor

Place

- Beach
- Park
- River
- Mexico
- School
- Church

Thing

- Ball
- Computer
- Book
- Pencil
- Trash Can
- Eraser
- Telephone

Mix-N-Match: Language Arts
Kagan Publishing • 1 (800) 933-2667 • www.KaganOnline.com

Compound Words

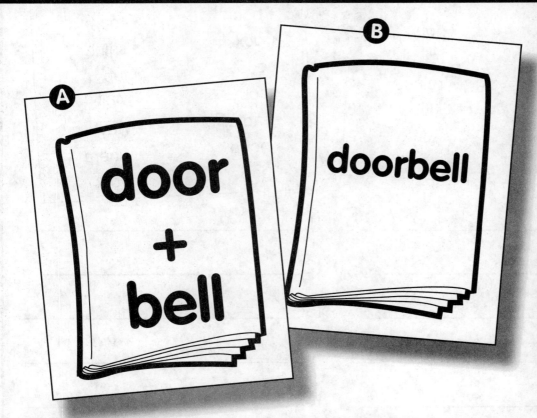

Students practice compound words by matching a compound word with its component words.

Quizzing Questions

► **A Cards: Components**
  • What compound word do I make?
► **B Cards: Compound Words**
  • What two words am I made of?

Mix-N-Match: Language Arts
Kagan Publishing • 1 (800) 933-2667 • www.KaganOnline.com

Compound Words

Write 20 compound words on the spaces below using a word from each Word Bank.

Word Bank 1

- after
- air
- base
- bath
- bed
- class
- door
- drive
- every
- finger
- home
- mail
- news
- note
- pop
- rail
- rain
- side
- some
- sun

Word Bank 2

- ball
- bell
- body
- book
- box
- coat
- corn
- mate
- noon
- paper
- plane
- print
- road
- room
- shine
- tub
- walk
- way
- where
- work

1._____

2._____

3._____

4._____

5._____

6._____

7._____

8._____

9._____

10._____

11._____

12._____

13._____

14._____

15._____

16._____

17._____

18._____

19._____

20._____

Mix-N-Match: Language Arts
Kagan Publishing • 1 (800) 933-2667 • www.KaganOnline.com

Compound Words

Break each compound word into two smaller words.

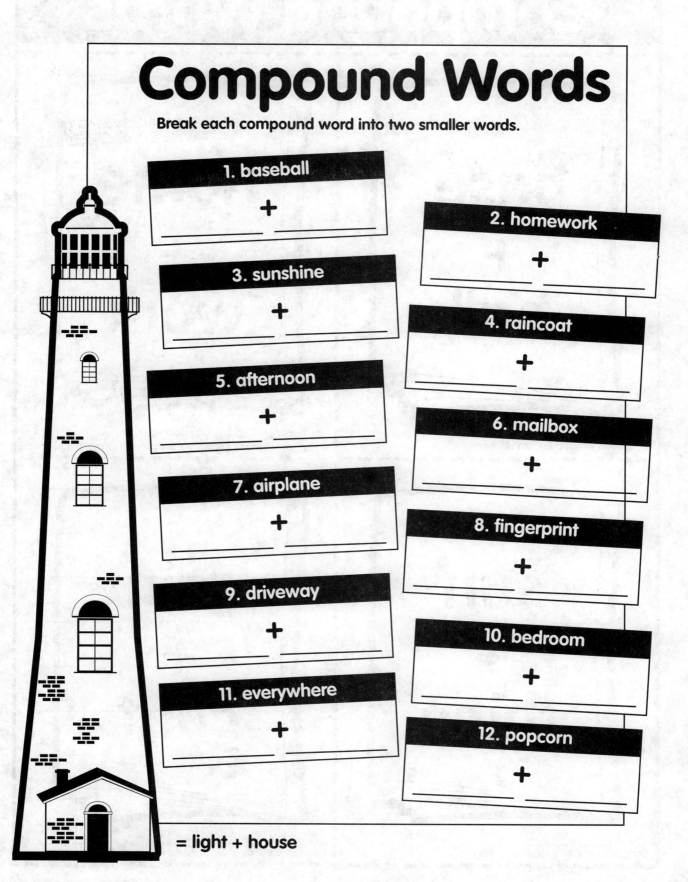

1. baseball

_____ + _____

2. homework

_____ + _____

3. sunshine

_____ + _____

4. raincoat

_____ + _____

5. afternoon

_____ + _____

6. mailbox

_____ + _____

7. airplane

_____ + _____

8. fingerprint

_____ + _____

9. driveway

_____ + _____

10. bedroom

_____ + _____

11. everywhere

_____ + _____

12. popcorn

_____ + _____

= light + house

Compound Words

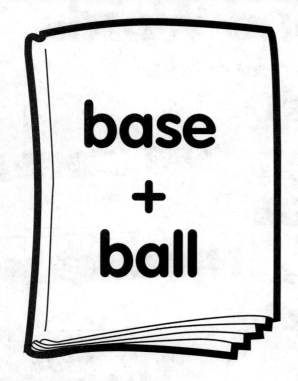

base

+

ball

home

+

work

sun

+

shine

rain

+

coat

Mix-N-Match: Language Arts
Kagan Publishing • 1 (800) 933-2667 • www.KaganOnline.com

Compound Words

baseball

Compound Words © Kagan Publishing

homework

Compound Words © Kagan Publishing

sunshine

Compound Words © Kagan Publishing

raincoat

Compound Words © Kagan Publishing

Compound Words

after + noon

mail + box

air + plane

finger + print

Mix-N-Match: Language Arts
Kagan Publishing • 1 (800) 933-2667 • www.KaganOnline.com

Compound Words

afternoon

mailbox

airplane

fingerprint

Compound Words

drive
+
way

bed
+
room

every
+
where

pop
+
corn

Compound Words

driveway

bedroom

everywhere

popcorn

Compound Words

note + book

door + bell

news + paper

bath + tub

Mix-N-Match: Language Arts
Kagan Publishing • 1 (800) 933-2667 • www.KaganOnline.com

Compound Words

notebook

doorbell

Compound Words © Kagan Publishing

Compound Words © Kagan Publishing

newspaper

bathtub

Compound Words © Kagan Publishing

Compound Words © Kagan Publishing

Compound Words

some
+
body

side
+
walk

rail
+
road

class
+
mate

Compound Words

somebody

sidewalk

railroad

classmate

Compound Words

1. base + ball .... baseball
2. home + work .... homework
3. sun + shine .... sunshine
4. rain + coat .... raincoat
5. after + noon.............................. afternoon
6. mail + box.................................. mailbox
7. air + plane .... airplane
8. finger + print .... fingerprint
9. drive + way................................ driveway
10. bed + room .... bedroom
11. every + where.......................... everywhere
12. pop + corn............................... popcorn
13. note + book............................. notebook
14. door + bell............................... doorbell
15. news + paper........................... newspaper
16. bath + tub................................ bathtub
17. some + body .... somebody
18. side + walk.............................. sidewalk
19. rail + road................................ railroad
20. class + mate............................ classmate

Mix-N-Match: Language Arts
Kagan Publishing • 1 (800) 933-2667 • www.KaganOnline.com

Contractions

Students practice contractions by matching the phrase with its contraction.

Quizzing Questions

▶ **A Cards: Phrases**
- What is my contraction?
- Where does the apostrophe go?

▶ **B Cards: Contractions**
- What phrase do I represent?
- What letters are missing?

Contractions

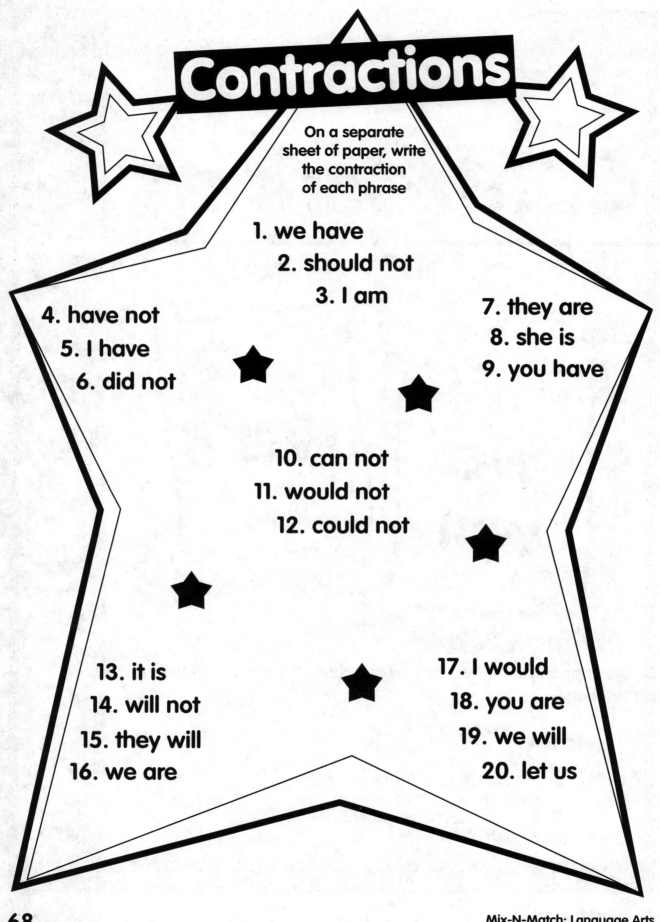

On a separate sheet of paper, write the contraction of each phrase

1. we have
2. should not
3. I am

4. have not
5. I have
6. did not

7. they are
8. she is
9. you have

10. can not
11. would not
12. could not

13. it is
14. will not
15. they will
16. we are

17. I would
18. you are
19. we will
20. let us

Mix-N-Match: Language Arts
Kagan Publishing • 1 (800) 933-2667 • www.KaganOnline.com

Contractions

Write the phrase represented by each contraction on the line provided.

1 I'm_____

2 she's_____

3 we're_____

4 you're_____

5 I've_____

6 you've_____

7 we've_____

8 they'll_____

9 it's_____

10 won't_____

11 let's_____

12 can't_____

13 I'd_____

14 they're_____

15 we'll_____

16 haven't_____

17 shouldn't_____

18 didn't_____

19 wouldn't_____

20 couldn't_____

Contractions

I
am

she
is

we
are

you
are

Mix-N-Match: Language Arts
Kagan Publishing • 1 (800) 933-2667 • www.KaganOnline.com

Contractions

I'm

she's

we're

you're

Contractions © Kagan Publishing

Contractions © Kagan Publishing

Contractions © Kagan Publishing

Contractions © Kagan Publishing

Contractions

I have

you have

we have

they will

Mix-N-Match: Language Arts
Kagan Publishing • 1 (800) 933-2667 • www.KaganOnline.com

Contractions

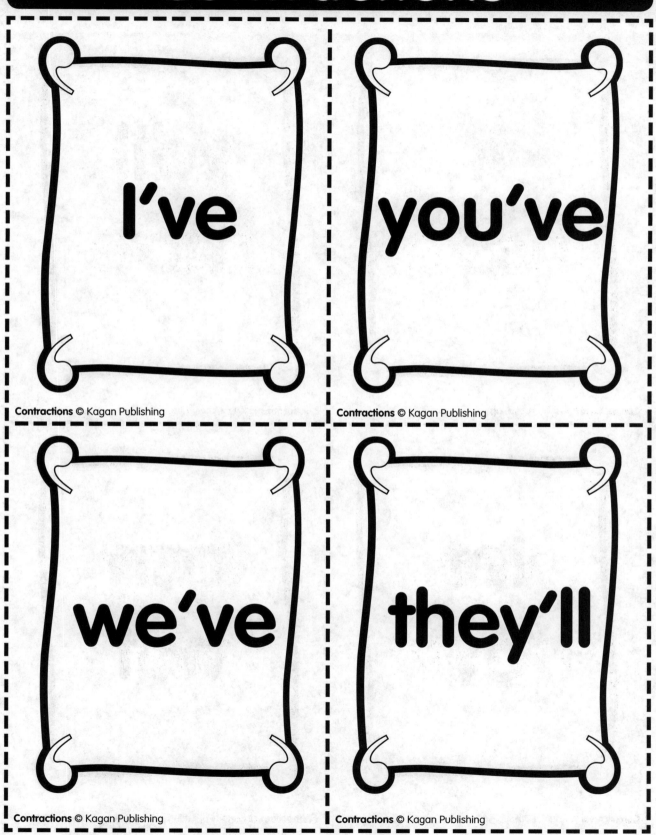

I've

you've

Contractions © Kagan Publishing

Contractions © Kagan Publishing

we've

they'll

Contractions © Kagan Publishing

Contractions © Kagan Publishing

Contractions

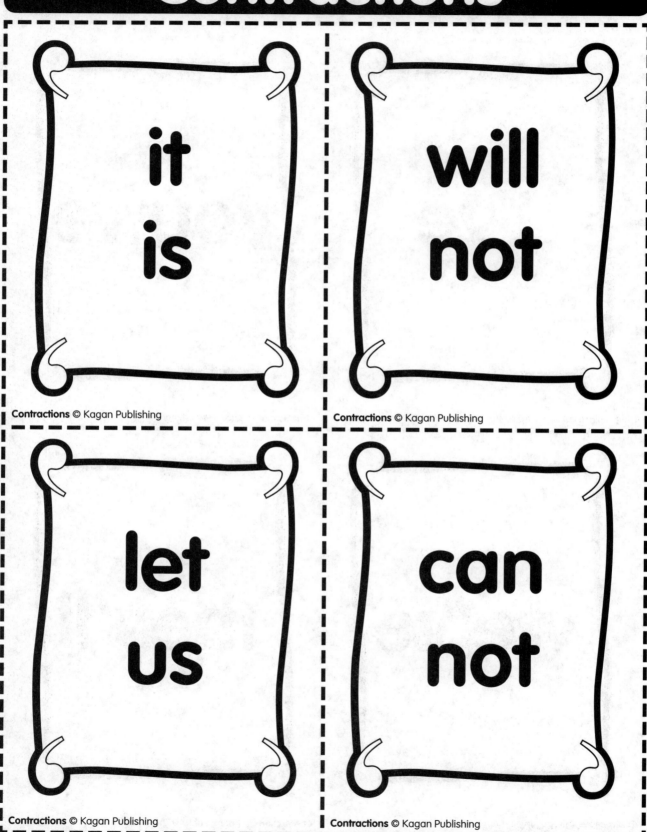

it
is

Contractions © Kagan Publishing

will
not

Contractions © Kagan Publishing

let
us

Contractions © Kagan Publishing

can
not

Contractions © Kagan Publishing

Mix-N-Match: Language Arts
Kagan Publishing • 1 (800) 933-2667 • www.KaganOnline.com

Contractions

it's

won't

Contractions © Kagan Publishing

Contractions © Kagan Publishing

let's

can't

Contractions © Kagan Publishing

Contractions © Kagan Publishing

Contractions

I would

they are

Contractions © Kagan Publishing

Contractions © Kagan Publishing

we will

have not

Contractions © Kagan Publishing

Contractions © Kagan Publishing

Mix-N-Match: Language Arts
Kagan Publishing • 1 (800) 933-2667 • www.KaganOnline.com

Contractions

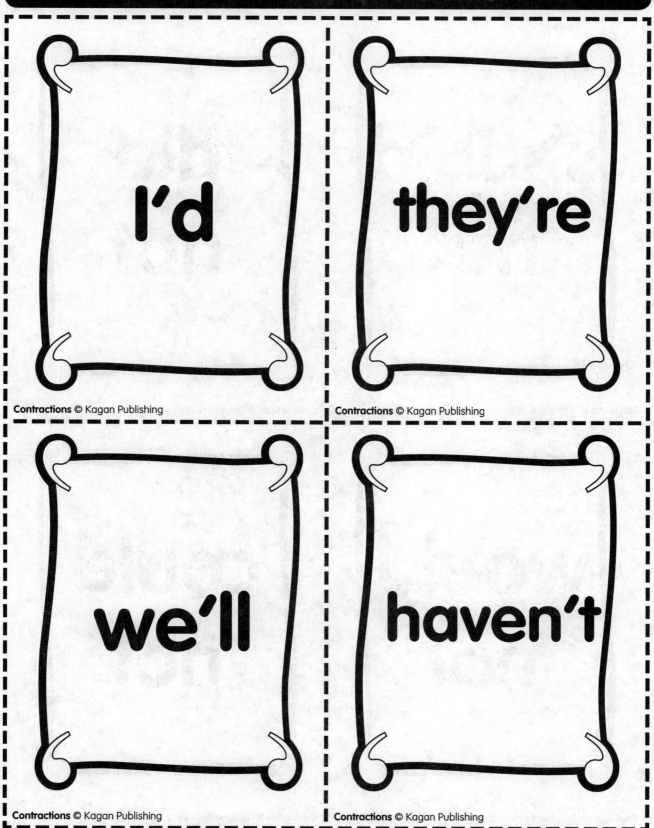

I'd

they're

Contractions © Kagan Publishing

Contractions © Kagan Publishing

we'll

haven't

Contractions © Kagan Publishing

Contractions © Kagan Publishing

Contractions

should
not

Contractions © Kagan Publishing

did
not

Contractions © Kagan Publishing

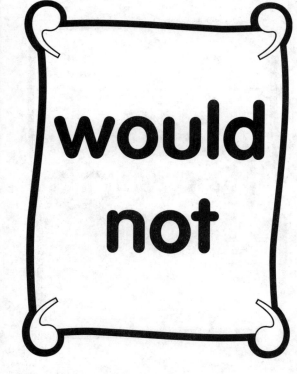

would
not

Contractions © Kagan Publishing

could
not

Contractions © Kagan Publishing

shouldn't

didn't

Contractions © Kagan Publishing

Contractions © Kagan Publishing

wouldn't

couldn't

Contractions © Kagan Publishing

Contractions © Kagan Publishing

Contractions

1. I am .... I'm
2. she is .... she's
3. we are .... we're
4. you are .... you're
5. I have .... I've
6. you have .... you've
7. we have .... we've
8. they will .... they'll
9. it is .... it's
10. will not .... won't
11. let us .... let's
12. can not .... can't
13. I would .... I'd
14. they are .... they're
15. we will .... we'll
16. have not .... haven't
17. should not .... shouldn't
18. did not .... didn't
19. would not .... wouldn't
20. could not .... couldn't

Mix-N-Match: Language Arts
Kagan Publishing • 1 (800) 933-2667 • www.KaganOnline.com

Dictionary Guide Words

Students practice locating words in a dictionary by matching a word with its dictionary guide words.

Quizzing Questions

- ▶ **A Cards: Dictionary Guide Words**
  - What is one word that you might find on my page?
- ▶ **B Cards: Words**
  - What are two possible guide words?

Mix-N-Match: Language Arts
Kagan Publishing • 1 (800) 933-2667 • www.KaganOnline.com

Dictionary Guide Words

What word from the word bank would you find on my page? Fill in the correct word from the word bank.

1. awake – axis_____

2. amuse – ancient_____

3. colony – colt_____

4. cactus – calculator_____

5. fable – face_____

6. fall – fancy_____

7. horse – hour_____

8. home – honor_____

9. letter – lie _____

10. mall – market_____

Word Bank

1. level

2. honey

3. family

4. hot

5. color

6. man

7. anchor

8. cage

9. award

10. fabric

Mix-N-Match: Language Arts
Kagan Publishing • 1 (800) 933-2667 • www.KaganOnline.com

Dictionary Guide Words

What page of the dictionary would you find the word on? Fill in the letter corresponding to the correct dictionary guide words.

1. might_____

2. odd_____

3. paper_____

4. pasta_____

5. razor_____

6. season_____

7. teach_____

8. teen_____

9. vapor_____

10. war_____

Dictionary Guide Words

A. **ocean – odor**

B. **tax - tear**

C. **pass – patch**

D. **tease – tender**

E. **middle – milk**

F. **raw – reach**

G. **walnut – warm**

H. **pants – parachute**

I. **sea - secret**

J. **vanilla – vase**

Dictionary Guide Words

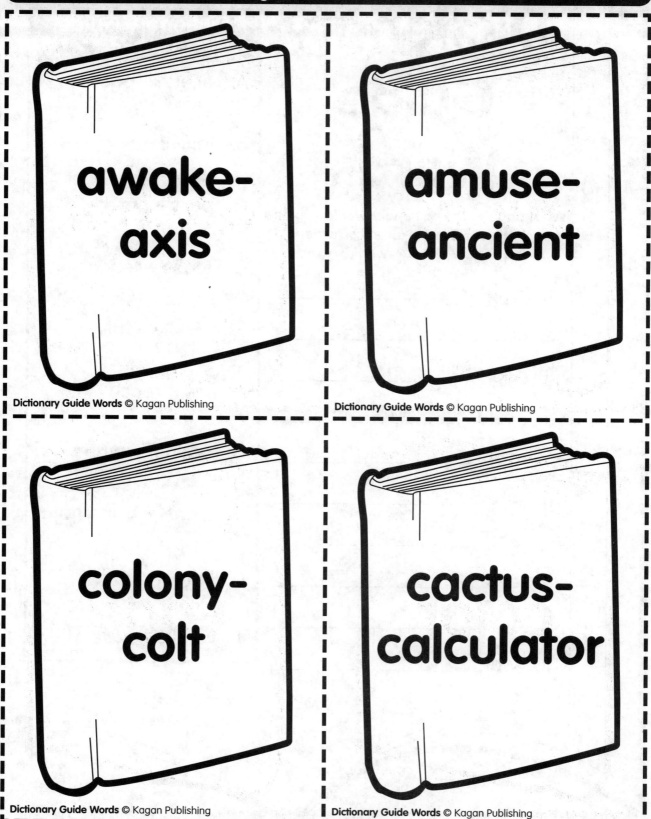

awake-
axis

Dictionary Guide Words © Kagan Publishing

amuse-
ancient

Dictionary Guide Words © Kagan Publishing

colony-
colt

Dictionary Guide Words © Kagan Publishing

cactus-
calculator

Dictionary Guide Words © Kagan Publishing

Mix-N-Match: Language Arts
Kagan Publishing • 1 (800) 933-2667 • www.KaganOnline.com

Dictionary Guide Words

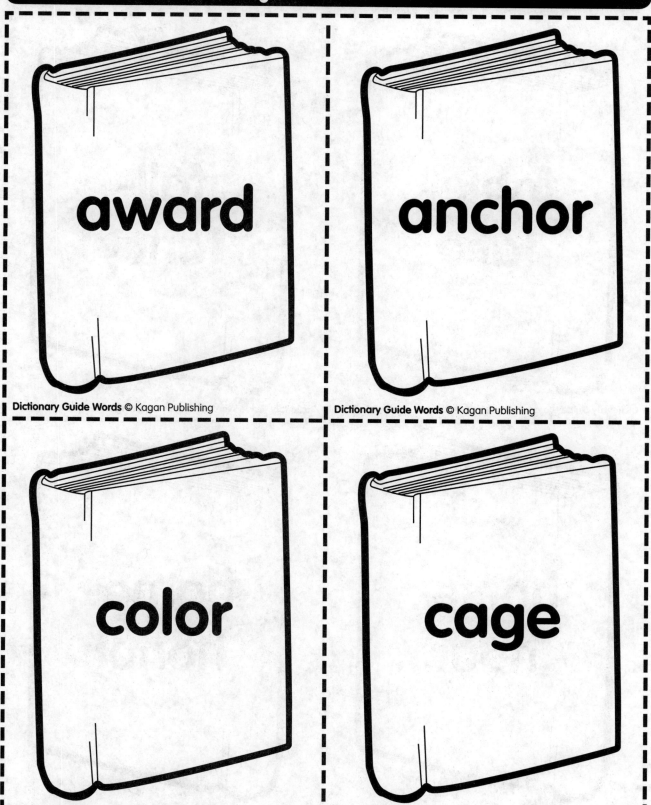

award

anchor

color

cage

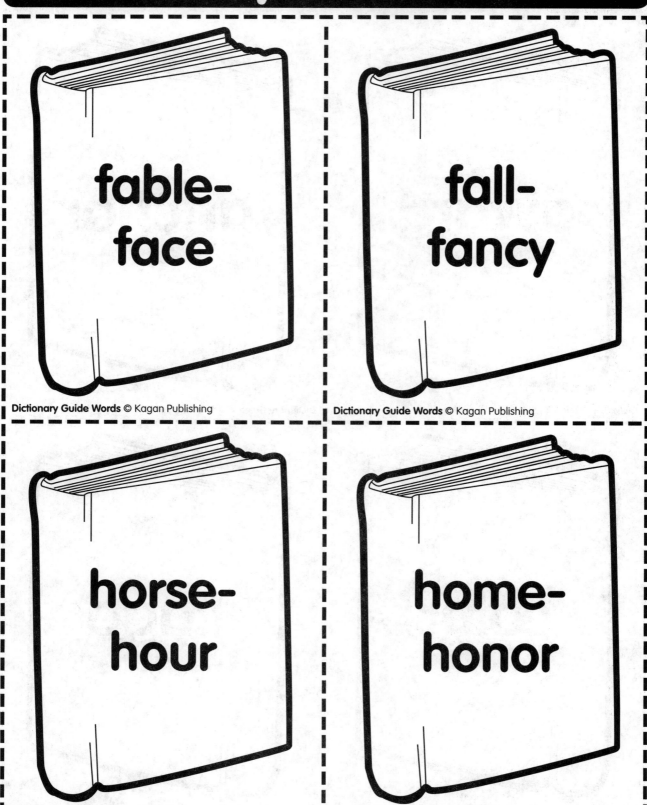

fable-
face

Dictionary Guide Words © Kagan Publishing

fall-
fancy

Dictionary Guide Words © Kagan Publishing

horse-
hour

Dictionary Guide Words © Kagan Publishing

home-
honor

Dictionary Guide Words © Kagan Publishing

fabric

Dictionary Guide Words © Kagan Publishing

family

Dictionary Guide Words © Kagan Publishing

hot

Dictionary Guide Words © Kagan Publishing

honey

Dictionary Guide Words © Kagan Publishing

Dictionary Guide Words

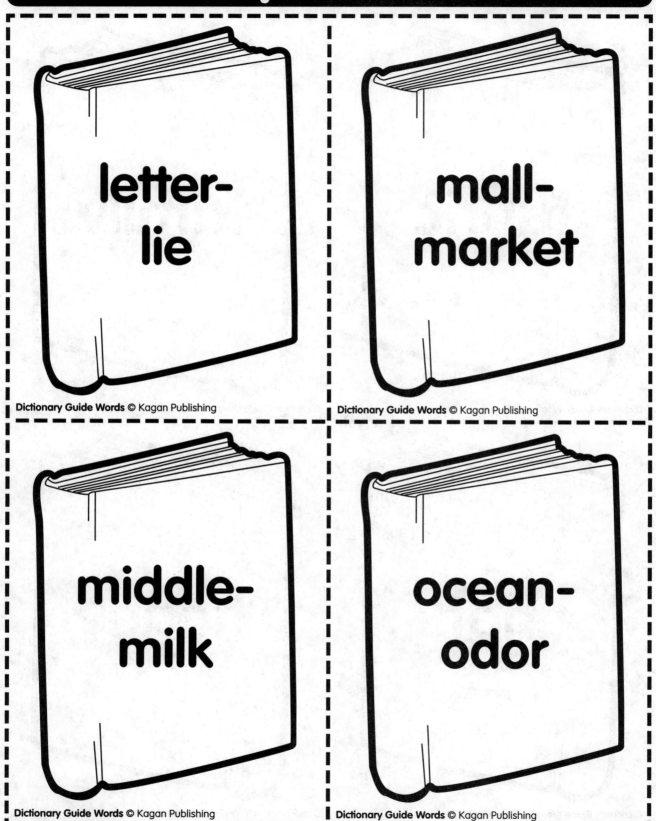

letter- lie

Dictionary Guide Words © Kagan Publishing

mall- market

Dictionary Guide Words © Kagan Publishing

middle- milk

Dictionary Guide Words © Kagan Publishing

ocean- odor

Dictionary Guide Words © Kagan Publishing

Dictionary Guide Words

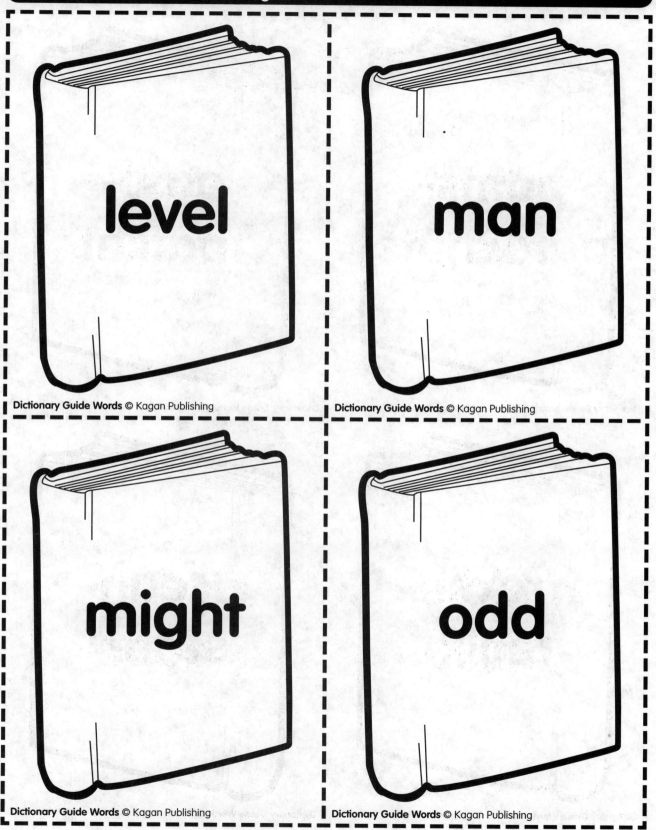

level

man

Dictionary Guide Words © Kagan Publishing

Dictionary Guide Words © Kagan Publishing

might

odd

Dictionary Guide Words © Kagan Publishing

Dictionary Guide Words © Kagan Publishing

Dictionary Guide Words

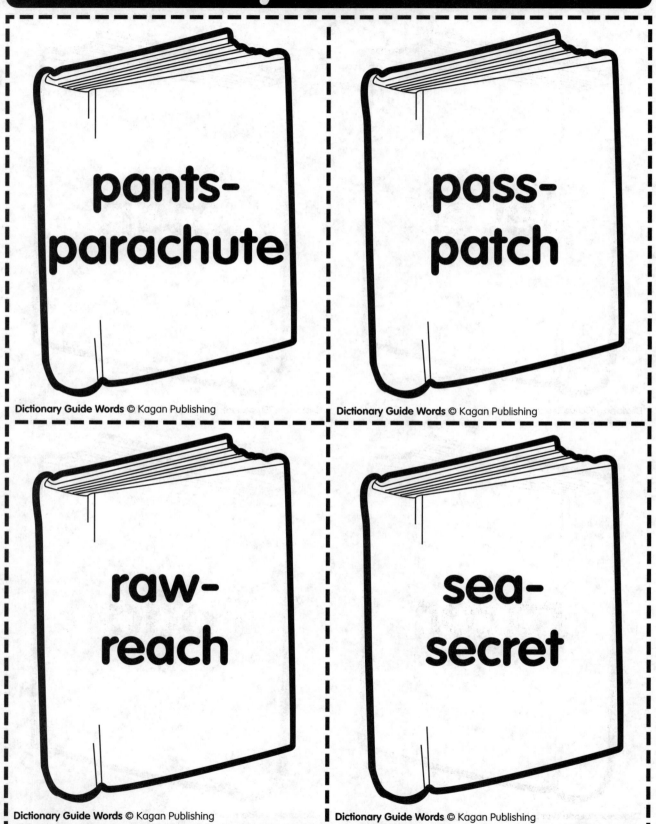

pants-
parachute

Dictionary Guide Words © Kagan Publishing

pass-
patch

Dictionary Guide Words © Kagan Publishing

raw-
reach

Dictionary Guide Words © Kagan Publishing

sea-
secret

Dictionary Guide Words © Kagan Publishing

Mix-N-Match: Language Arts
Kagan Publishing • 1 (800) 933-2667 • www.KaganOnline.com

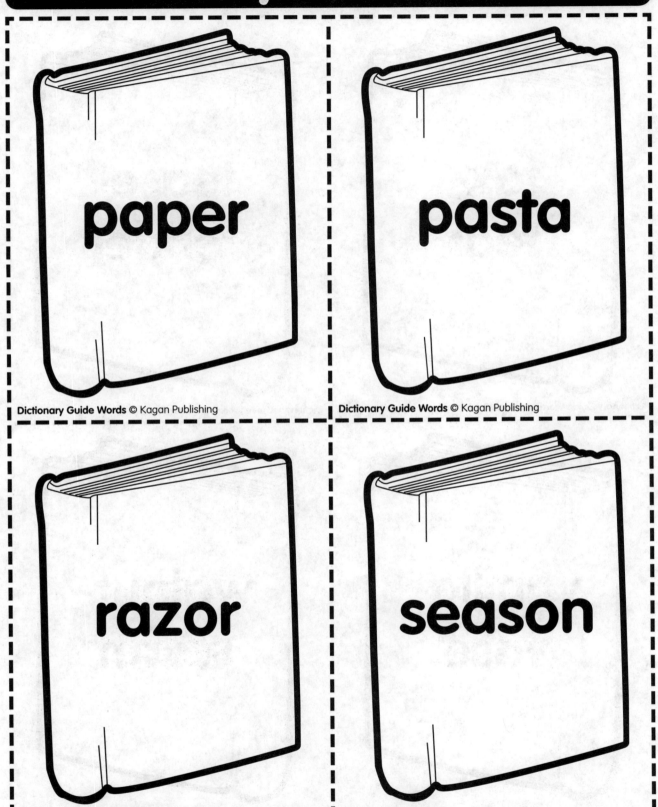

paper

pasta

Dictionary Guide Words © Kagan Publishing

Dictionary Guide Words © Kagan Publishing

razor

season

Dictionary Guide Words © Kagan Publishing

Dictionary Guide Words © Kagan Publishing

Dictionary Guide Words

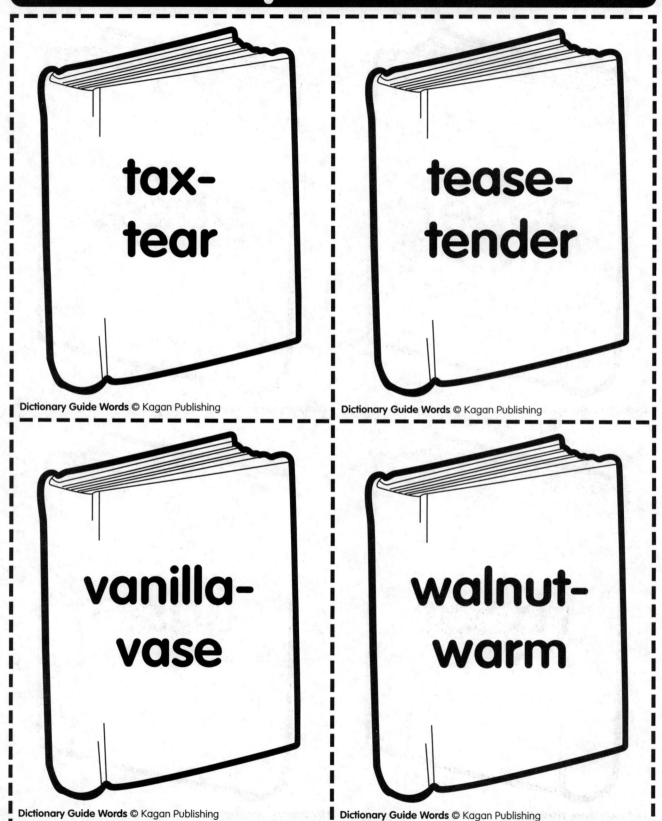

tax-
tear

Dictionary Guide Words © Kagan Publishing

tease-
tender

Dictionary Guide Words © Kagan Publishing

vanilla-
vase

Dictionary Guide Words © Kagan Publishing

walnut-
warm

Dictionary Guide Words © Kagan Publishing

Mix-N-Match: Language Arts
Kagan Publishing • 1 (800) 933-2667 • www.KaganOnline.com

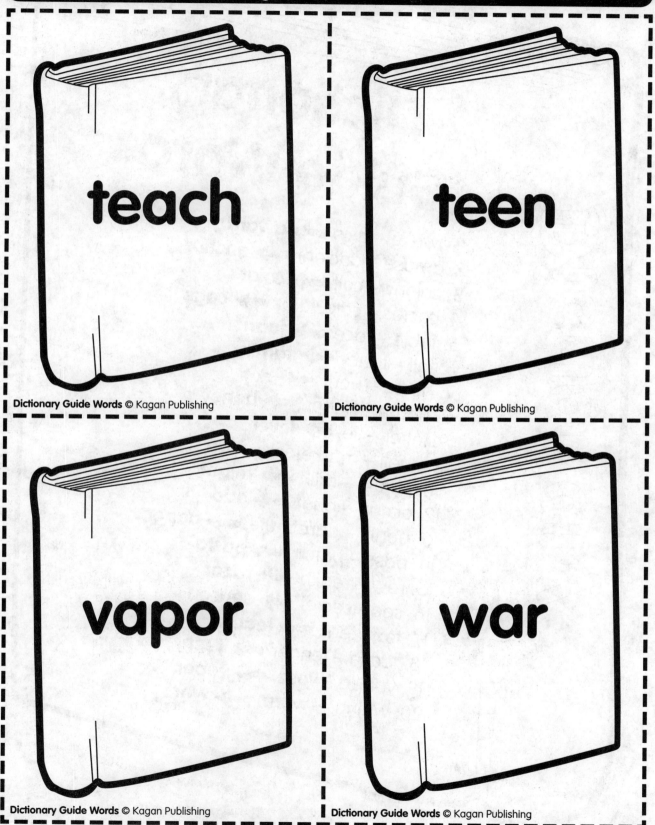

teach

Dictionary Guide Words © Kagan Publishing

teen

Dictionary Guide Words © Kagan Publishing

vapor

Dictionary Guide Words © Kagan Publishing

war

Dictionary Guide Words © Kagan Publishing

Dictionary Guide Words

1. awake – axis ➡ **award**
2. amuse – ancient ➡ **anchor**
3. colony – colt ➡ **color**
4. cactus – calculator ➡ **cage**
5. fable – face ➡ **fabric**
6. fall – fancy ➡ **family**
7. horse – hour ➡ **hot**
8. home – honor ➡ **honey**
9. letter – lie ➡ **level**
10. mall – market ➡ **man**
11. middle – milk ➡ **might**
12. ocean – odor ➡ **odd**
13. pants – parachute ➡ **paper**
14. pass – patch ➡ **pasta**
15. raw – reach ➡ **razor**
16. sea - secret ➡ **season**
17. tax - tear ➡ **teach**
18. tease – tender ➡ **teen**
19. vanilla – vase ➡ **vapor**
20. walnut – warm ➡ **war**

Dictionary

Mix-N-Match: Language Arts
Kagan Publishing • 1 (800) 933-2667 • www.KaganOnline.com

Double Letter Spelling Words

Double Letter Spelling Words

Students practice double letter spelling words by matching the word with the missing letters.

Quizzing Questions

▶ **A Cards: Words With Missing Double Letters**
  • What letters am I missing?
▶ **B Cards: Double Letters**
  • What is one word that uses these two letters?

Double Letter Spelling Words

Fill in the missing double letters.

1. bu__ __le

2. o__ __ur

3. pa__ __le

4. thr__ __

5. e__ __ect

6. gi__ __le

7. usua__ __y

8. spe__ __ing

9. swi__ __ing

10. su__ __y

11. ru__ __ing

12. sch__ __l

13. g__ __d

14. zi__ __er

15. wra__ __er

16. wo__ __y

17. le__ __

18. be__ __er

19. wri__ __en

20. fri__ __y

Mix-N-Match: Language Arts
Kagan Publishing • 1 (800) 933-2667 • www.KaganOnline.com

Double Letter Spelling Words

Write a word that has the double letters in it.

1. bb _____   9. nn _____

2. cc _____   10. oo _____

3. dd _____   11. pp _____

4. ee _____   12. rr _____

5. ff _____   13. ss _____

6. gg _____   14. tt _____

7. ll _____   15. zz _____

8. mm _____

Double Letter Spelling Words

bu_ _le

o_ _ur

pa_ _le

thr_ _

Double Letter Spelling Words

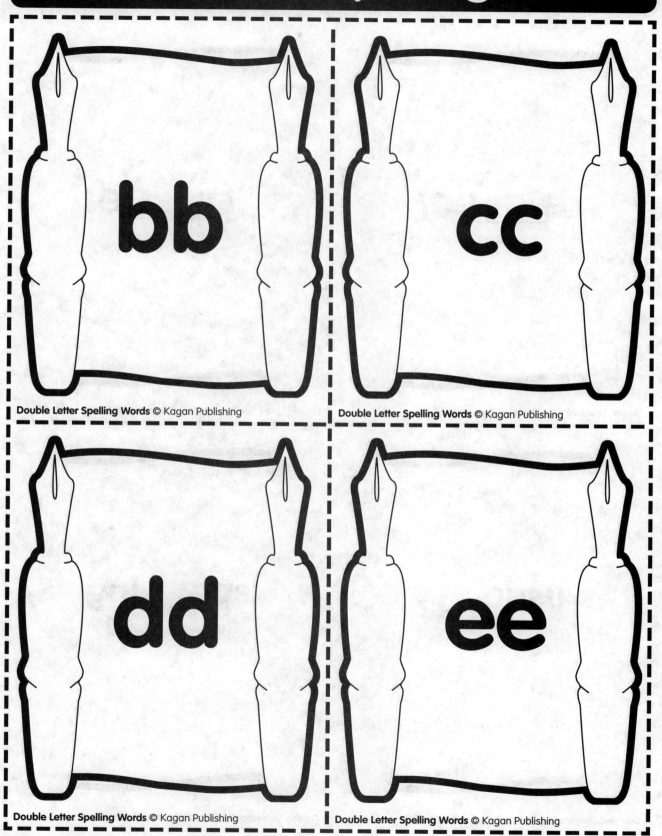

bb

Double Letter Spelling Words © Kagan Publishing

cc

Double Letter Spelling Words © Kagan Publishing

dd

Double Letter Spelling Words © Kagan Publishing

ee

Double Letter Spelling Words © Kagan Publishing

Double Letter Spelling Words

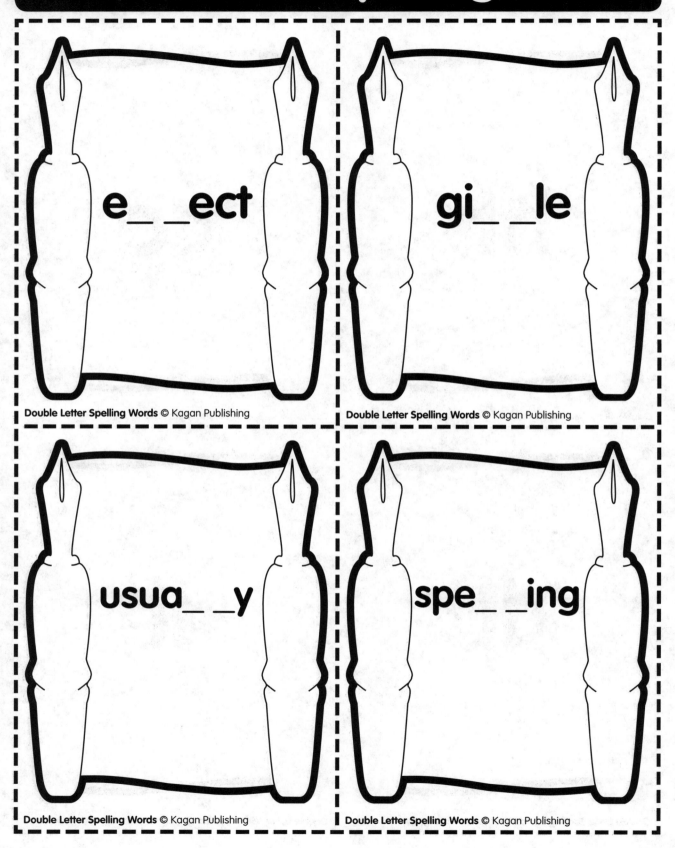

e_ _ect

Double Letter Spelling Words © Kagan Publishing

gi_ _le

Double Letter Spelling Words © Kagan Publishing

usua_ _y

Double Letter Spelling Words © Kagan Publishing

spe_ _ing

Double Letter Spelling Words © Kagan Publishing

Mix-N-Match: Language Arts
Kagan Publishing • 1 (800) 933-2667 • www.KaganOnline.com

Double Letter Spelling Words

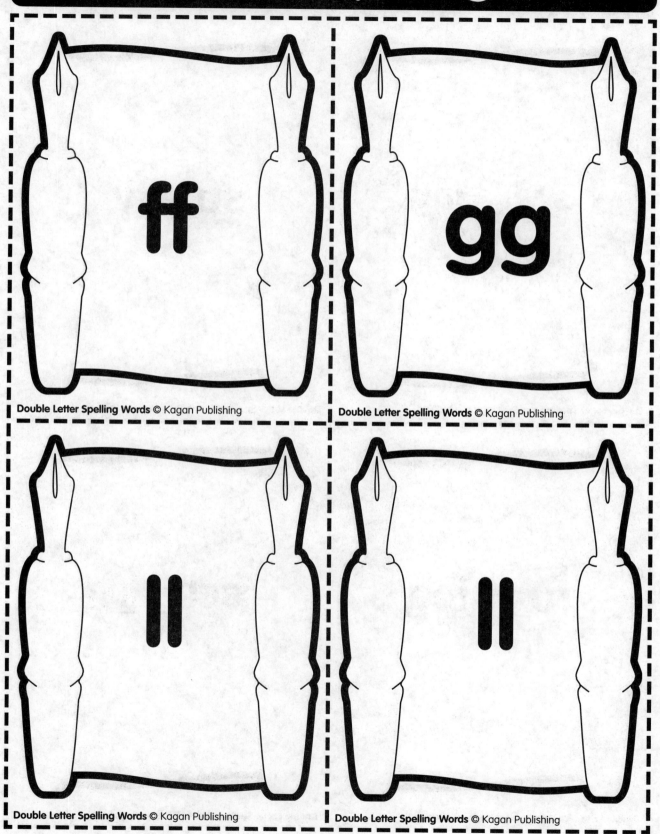

Double Letter Spelling Words © Kagan Publishing

ff

Double Letter Spelling Words © Kagan Publishing

gg

Double Letter Spelling Words © Kagan Publishing

ll

Double Letter Spelling Words © Kagan Publishing

ll

Double Letter Spelling Words

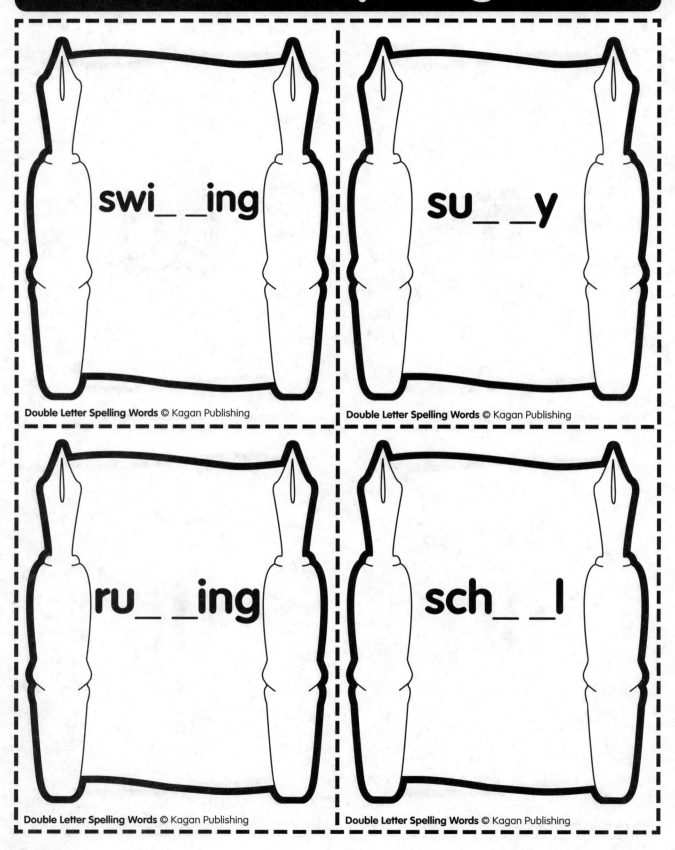

swi_ _ing

su_ _y

ru_ _ing

sch_ _l

Mix-N-Match: Language Arts
Kagan Publishing • 1 (800) 933-2667 • www.KaganOnline.com

Double Letter Spelling Words

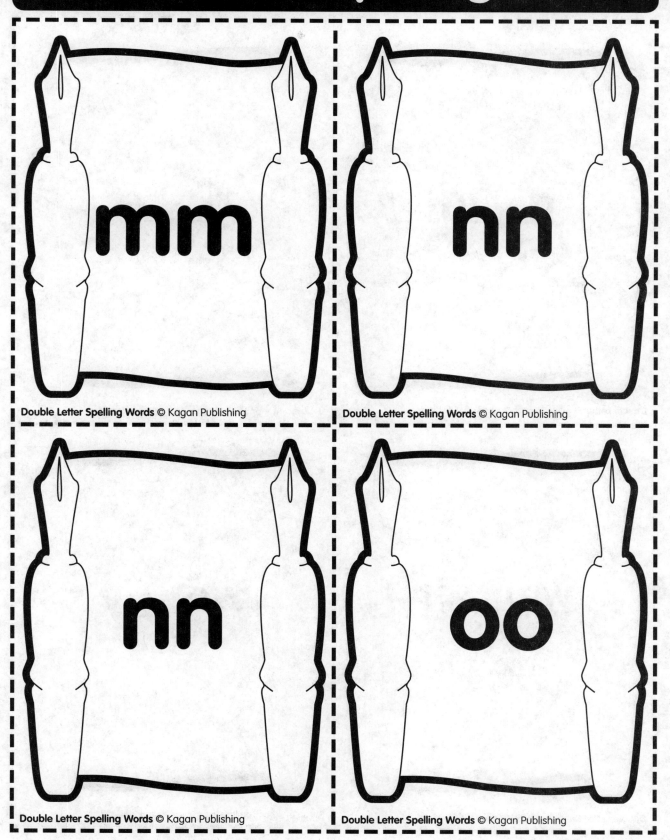

Double Letter Spelling Words © Kagan Publishing

Double Letter Spelling Words © Kagan Publishing

Double Letter Spelling Words © Kagan Publishing

Double Letter Spelling Words © Kagan Publishing

Double Letter Spelling Words

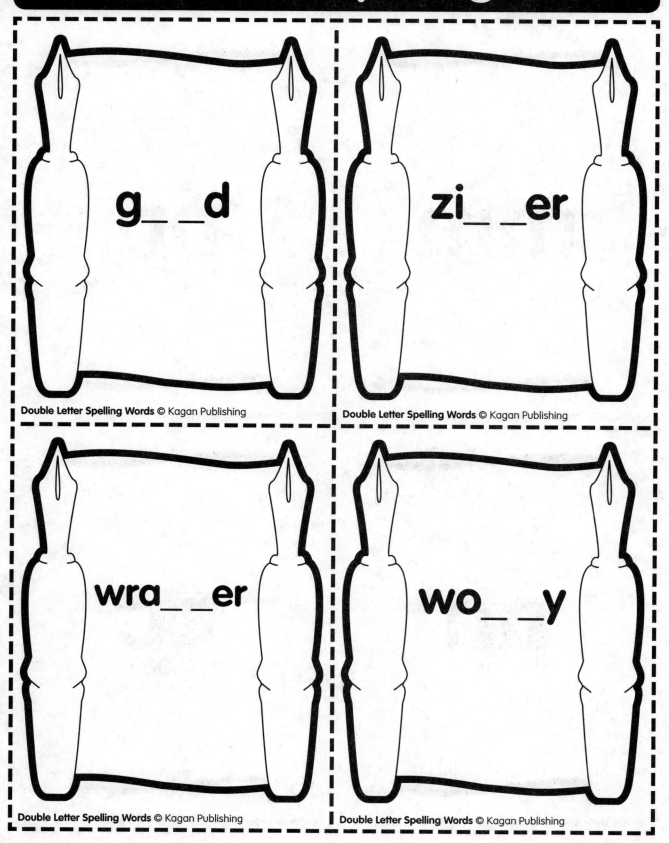

g_ _d

zi_ _er

wra_ _er

wo_ _y

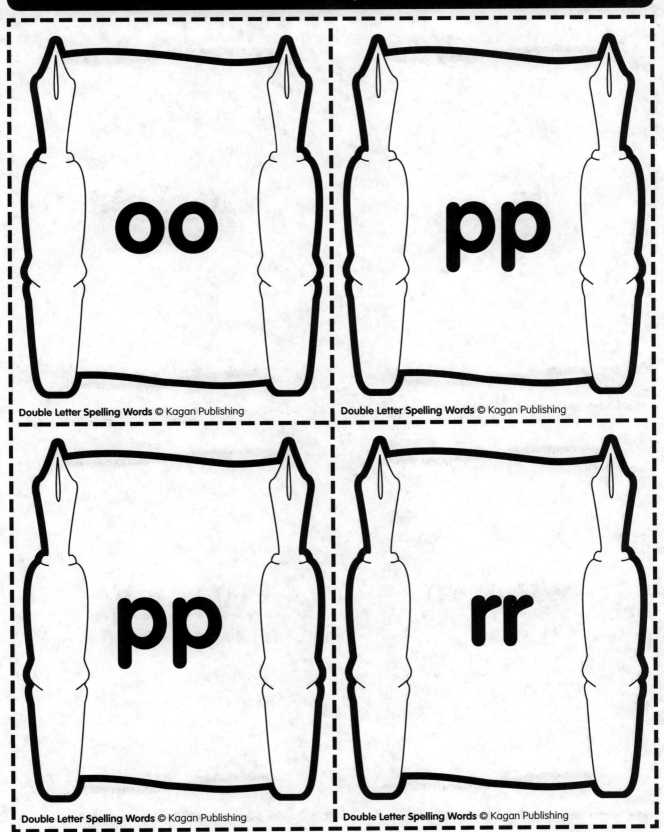

oo

Double Letter Spelling Words © Kagan Publishing

pp

Double Letter Spelling Words © Kagan Publishing

pp

Double Letter Spelling Words © Kagan Publishing

rr

Double Letter Spelling Words © Kagan Publishing

Double Letter Spelling Words

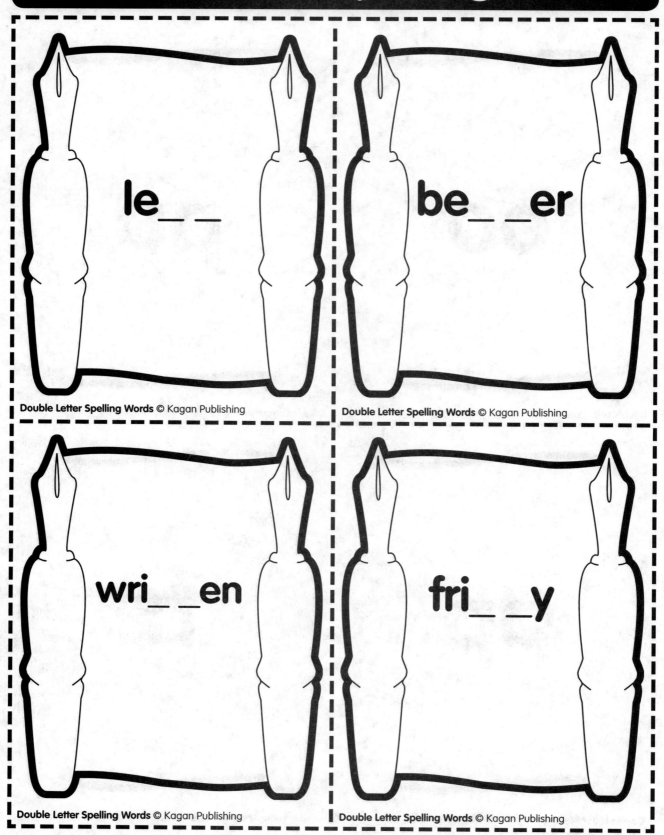

le_ _

be_ _er

wri_ _en

fri_ _y

Mix-N-Match: Language Arts
Kagan Publishing • 1 (800) 933-2667 • www.KaganOnline.com

Double Letter Spelling Words

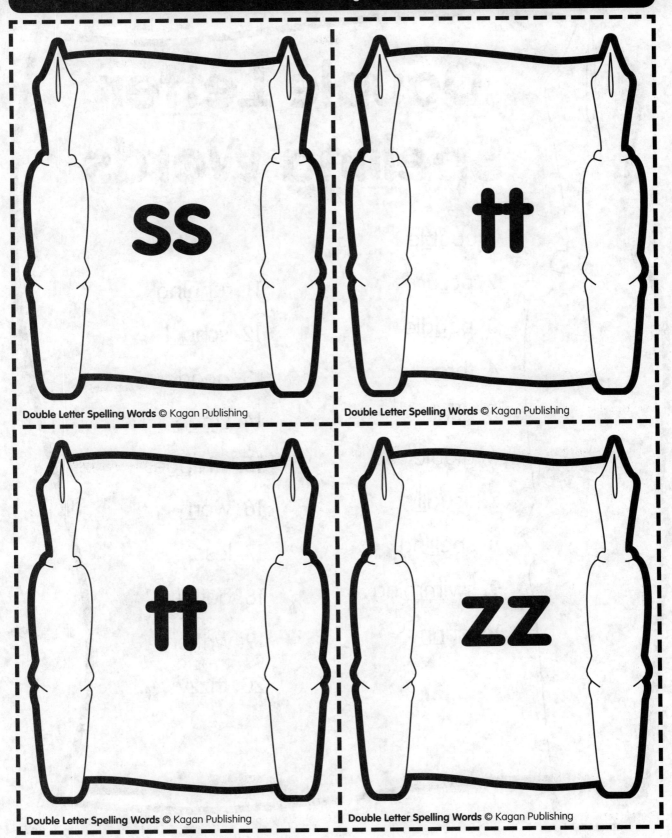

ss

tt

tt

zz

Double Letter Spelling Words

1. bu<u>bb</u>le
2. o<u>cc</u>ur
3. pa<u>dd</u>le
4. thr<u>ee</u>
5. e<u>ff</u>ect
6. gi<u>gg</u>le
7. usua<u>ll</u>y
8. spe<u>ll</u>ing
9. swi<u>mm</u>ing
10. su<u>nn</u>y
11. ru<u>nn</u>ing
12. sch<u>oo</u>l
13. g<u>oo</u>d
14. zi<u>pp</u>er
15. wra<u>pp</u>er
16. wo<u>rr</u>y
17. le<u>ss</u>
18. be<u>tt</u>er
19. wri<u>tt</u>en
20. fri<u>zz</u>y

Mix-N-Match: Language Arts
Kagan Publishing • 1 (800) 933-2667 • www.KaganOnline.com

Fact or Opinion

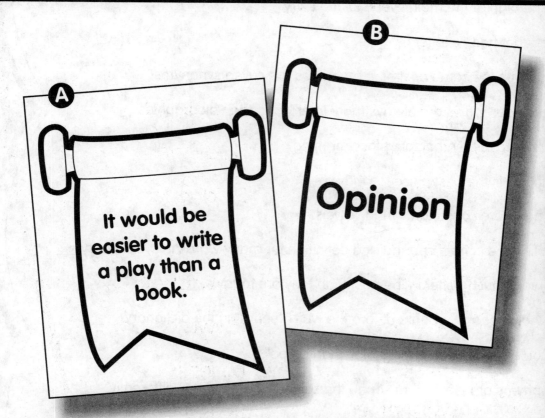

Students practice distinguishing fact from opinion by determining if the statement is a fact or an opinion.

Quizzing Questions

▶ **A Cards: Statements**
  • Is this statement a fact or opinion?
▶ **B Cards: Fact or Opinion**
  • Can you give me an example of a fact (or opinion)?

Fact or Opinion

After each statement, write <u>F</u> if it is a fact or <u>O</u> if it is an opinion.

1. Reading is fun.___

2. A biography is a written history of someone's life.___

3. Mystery stories are better than love stories.___

4. A plot is the plan or the main events of the story.___

5. The alphabet has 26 letters.___

6. Words with the same or similar meanings are called synonyms.___

7. Autobiographies are always more interesting than biographies.___

8. A noun can be a person, place, or thing.___

9. The library is the best place to study.___

10. There are more consonants than vowels.___

11. You can find the correct spelling and definition for many words in a dictionary.___

12. Poets were much better in the past than they are today.___

13. The word "book" appears before the word "pencil" in the dictionary.___

14. It would be easier to write a play than a book.___

15. Homonyms are words that sound the same but are spelled differently.___

16. The fastest way to become a better writer is to read.___

17. Antonyms are words of opposite meanings.___

18. Rules of grammar state that a comma must never be used to end a sentence.___

19. Shakespeare was the best writer who ever lived.___

20. Writing based in truth is called nonfiction.___

Mix-N-Match: Language Arts
Kagan Publishing • 1 (800) 933-2667 • www.KaganOnline.com

Fact or Opinion

Write six statements: Three facts and three opinions. Read them to a partner and let him or her determine which are facts and which are opinions. Then listen to your partner's statements and determine which are facts and which are opinions.

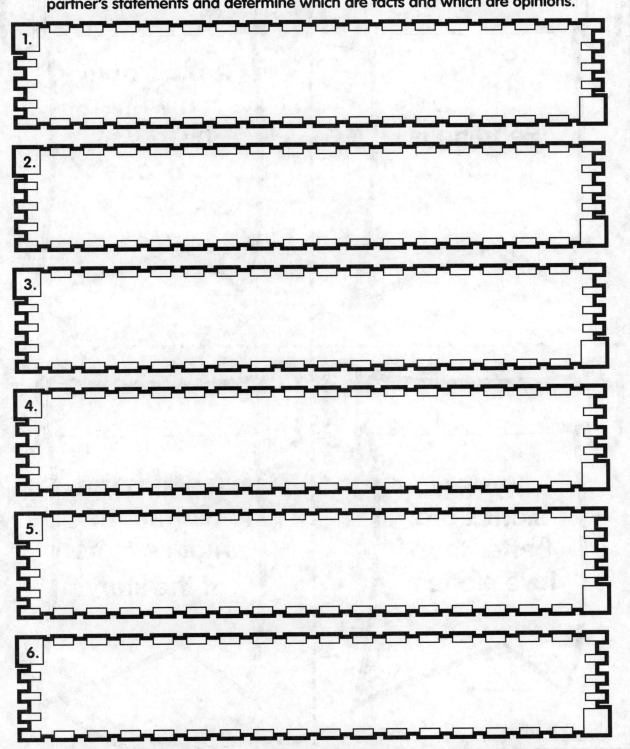

1.

2.

3.

4.

5.

6.

Fact or Opinion

Reading is fun.

A biography is a written history of someone's life.

Mystery stories are better than love stories.

A plot is the plan or the main events of the story.

Fact or Opinion

Opinion

Fact

Opinion

Fact

Fact or Opinion

The alphabet has 26 letters.

Words with the same or similar meanings are called synonyms.

Autobiographies are always more interesting than biographies.

A noun can be a person, place, or thing.

Mix-N-Match: Language Arts
Kagan Publishing • 1 (800) 933-2667 • www.KaganOnline.com

Fact or Opinion

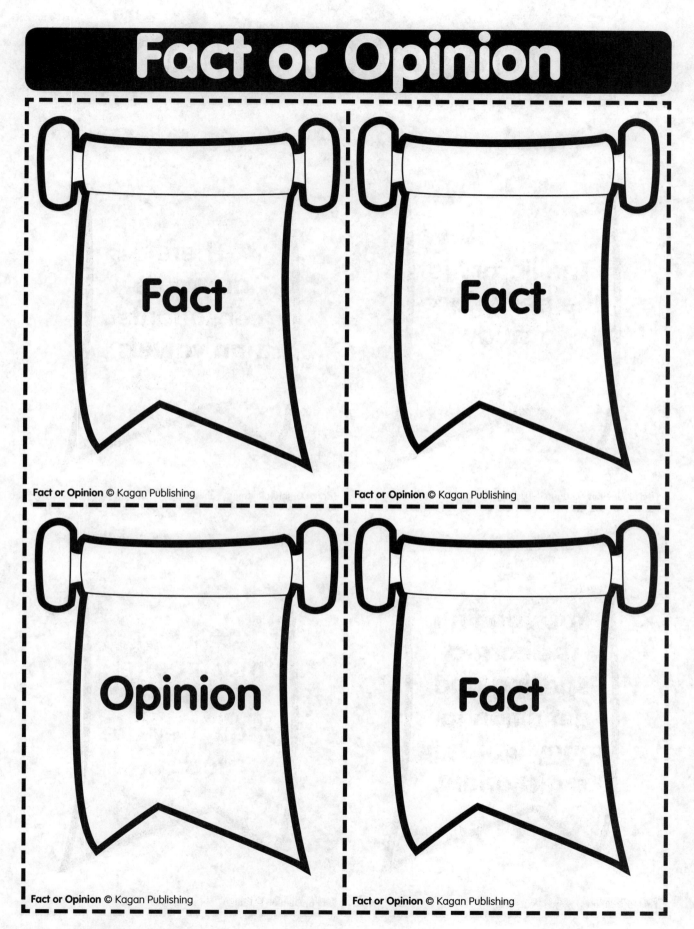

Fact

Fact

Opinion

Fact

Fact or Opinion © Kagan Publishing

Fact or Opinion © Kagan Publishing

Fact or Opinion © Kagan Publishing

Fact or Opinion © Kagan Publishing

Fact or Opinion

The library is the best place to study.

There are more consonants than vowels.

You can find the correct spelling and definition for many words in a dictionary.

Poets were much better in the past than they are today.

Mix-N-Match: Language Arts
Kagan Publishing • 1 (800) 933-2667 • www.KaganOnline.com

Fact or Opinion

Opinion

Fact

Fact

Opinion

Fact or Opinion

The word "book" appears be- fore the word "pencil" in the dictionary.

It would be easier to write a play than a book.

Homonyms are words that sound the same but are spelled differently.

The fastest way to become a better writer is to read.

Mix-N-Match: Language Arts
Kagan Publishing • 1 (800) 933-2667 • www.KaganOnline.com

Fact or Opinion

Fact

Opinion

Fact

Opinion

Fact or Opinion

Antonyms are words of opposite meanings.

Rules of grammar state that a comma must never be used to end a sentence.

Shakespeare was the best writer who ever lived.

Writing based in truth is called nonfiction.

Mix-N-Match: Language Arts
Kagan Publishing • 1 (800) 933-2667 • www.KaganOnline.com

Fact or Opinion

Fact

Fact

Opinion

Fact

Fact or Opinion

1. Reading is fun. **Opinion**
2. A biography is a written history of someone's life. **Fact**
3. Mystery stories are better than love stories. **Opinion**
4. A plot is the plan or the main events of the story. **Fact**
5. The alphabet has 26 letters. **Fact**
6. Words with the same or similar meanings are called synonyms. **Fact**
7. Autobiographies are always more interesting than biographies. **Opinion**
8. A noun can be a person, place, or thing. **Fact**
9. The library is the best place to study. **Opinion**
10. There are more consonants than vowels. **Fact**
11. You can find the correct spelling and definition for many words in a dictionary. **Fact**
12. Poets were much better in the past than they are today. **Opinion**
13. The word "book" appears before the word "pencil" in the dictionary. **Fact**
14. It would be easier to write a play than a book. **Opinion**
15. Homonyms are words that sound the same but are spelled differently. **Fact**
16. The fastest way to become a better writer is to read. **Opinion**
17. Antonyms are words of opposite meanings. **Fact**
18. Rules of grammar state that a comma must never be used to end a sentence. **Fact**
19. Shakespeare was the best writer who ever lived. **Opinion**
20. Writing based in truth is called nonfiction. **Fact**

Mix-N-Match: Language Arts
Kagan Publishing • 1 (800) 933-2667 • www.KaganOnline.com

Homonyms

Students practice homonyms by matching a word with its homonym.

Quizzing Questions

▶ **A Cards: Homonym 1**
  • What does this word mean?
  • What is my homonym?
▶ **B Cards: Homonym 2**
  • How do you spell my homonym?
  • What does my homonym mean?

Mix-N-Match: Language Arts
Kagan Publishing • 1 (800) 933-2667 • www.KaganOnline.com

Homonyms

night

Write the homonym for each word.
When finished, take turns defining each word with a partner.

1. there_____   11. sea _____

2. wear _____   12. pain _____

3. hear_____   13. tide_____

4. right_____   14. toe _____

5. eight _____   15. hole _____

6. bare_____   16. night_____

7. knot _____   17. stair _____

8. tail _____   18. flea _____

9. buy _____   19. fair _____

10. know _____   20. need _____

knight

124

Select the correct word for each sentence or question.

1. I left my sweater over _____ . (there, their)

2. What are you going to _____ to the party? (wear, where)

3. I left my book right _____. (hear, here)

4. Tomorrow I will _____ to my pen pal. (right, write)

5. We were so hungry, so we just went home and _____ . (eight, ate)

6. In the forest, we saw a brown _____. (bare, bear)

7. The sailor tied a _____ in the rope. (knot, not)

8. The bunny has such a fluffy _____.(tail, tale)

9. What are you going to _____ mom for christmas? (buy, bye)

10. We have to go shopping because there is _____ more milk. (know, no)

11. I got glasses so I can _____ better. (sea, see)

12. When I broke my wrist, I was in _____ . (pain, pane)

13. At high _____ the water covers these rocks. (tide, tied)

14. We had to _____ the car when it got a flat tire. (toe, tow)

15. The gopher went back into its _____. (hole, whole)

16. The desert gets cold at_____. (knight, night)

17. It's rude to _____ (stair stare)

18. When animals are scared they often fight or_____. (flea, flee)

19. How much is the bus_____. (fair, fare)

20. Do you really _____ three bikes? (need, knead)

Homonyms

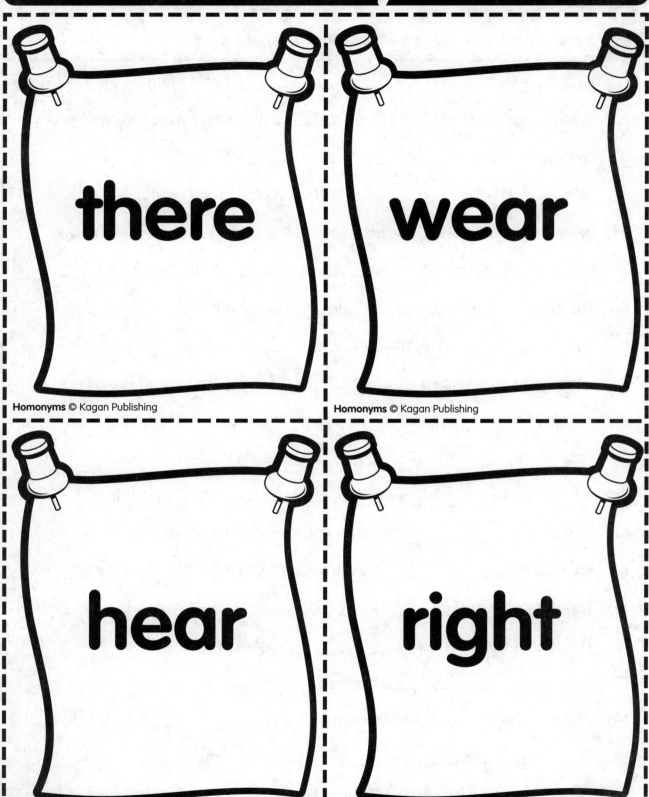

there

Homonyms © Kagan Publishing

wear

Homonyms © Kagan Publishing

hear

Homonyms © Kagan Publishing

right

Homonyms © Kagan Publishing

Mix-N-Match: Language Arts
Kagan Publishing • 1 (800) 933-2667 • www.KaganOnline.com

Homonyms

their

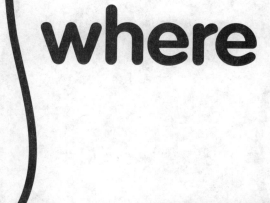

where

here

write

Homonyms

eight

bare

knot

tail

Homonyms © Kagan Publishing

Homonyms © Kagan Publishing

Homonyms © Kagan Publishing

Homonyms © Kagan Publishing

Mix-N-Match: Language Arts
Kagan Publishing • 1 (800) 933-2667 • www.KaganOnline.com

Homonyms

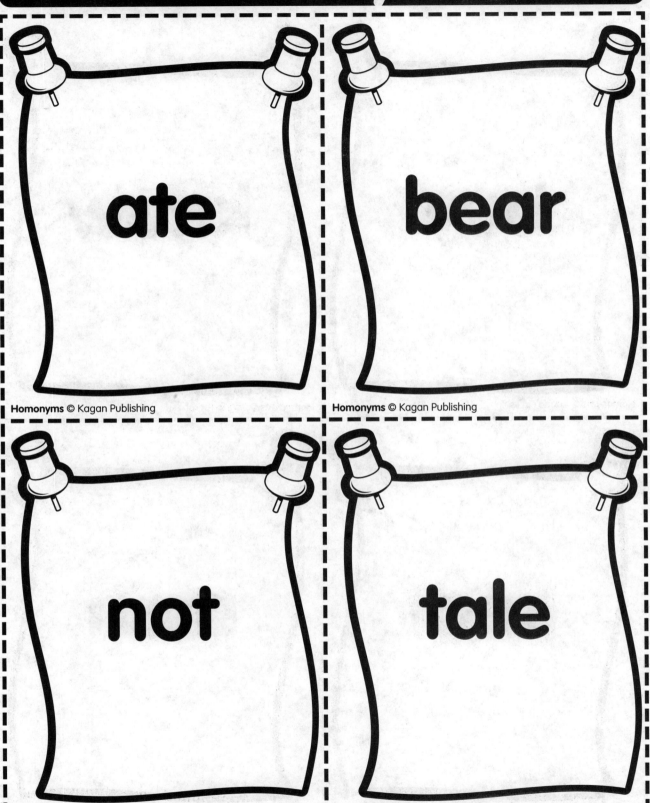

ate

bear

Homonyms © Kagan Publishing

Homonyms © Kagan Publishing

not

tale

Homonyms © Kagan Publishing

Homonyms © Kagan Publishing

Homonyms

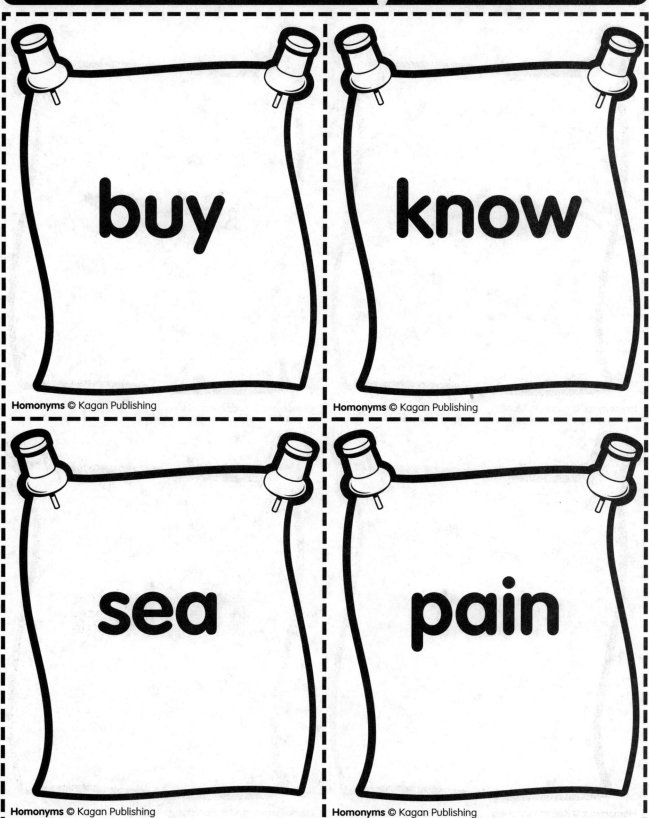

buy

know

sea

pain

Mix-N-Match: Language Arts
Kagan Publishing • 1 (800) 933-2667 • www.KaganOnline.com

Homonyms

bye

no

see

pane

Homonyms

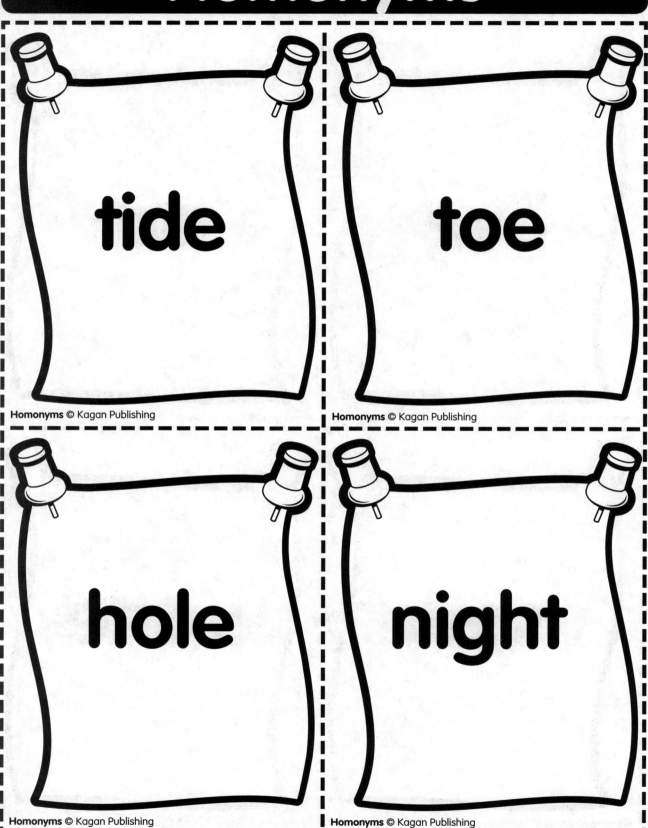

tide

toe

hole

night

Homonyms © Kagan Publishing

Homonyms © Kagan Publishing

Homonyms © Kagan Publishing

Homonyms © Kagan Publishing

Mix-N-Match: Language Arts
Kagan Publishing • 1 (800) 933-2667 • www.KaganOnline.com

Homonyms

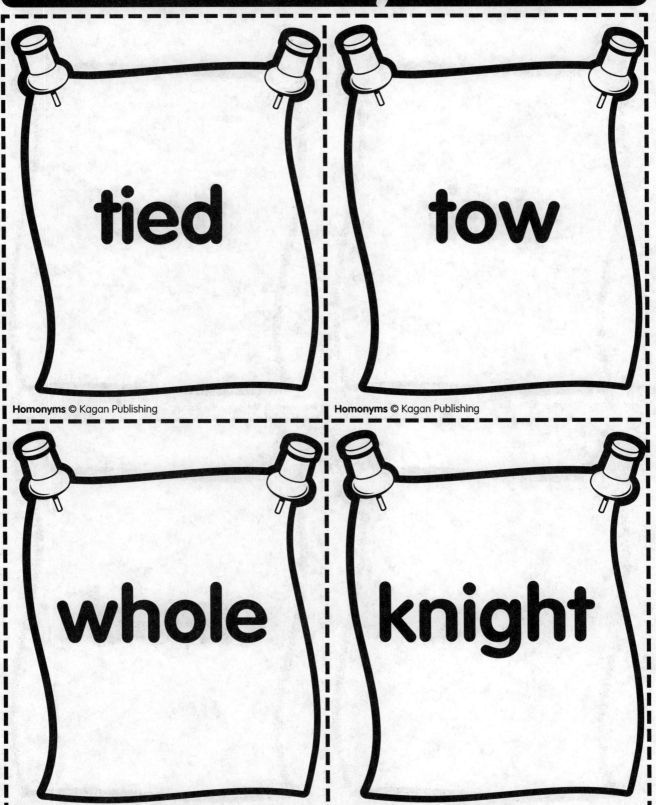

tied

tow

Homonyms © Kagan Publishing

Homonyms © Kagan Publishing

whole

knight

Homonyms © Kagan Publishing

Homonyms © Kagan Publishing

Kagan Publishing • 1 (800) 933-2667 • www.KaganOnline.com

Homonyms

stair

flea

Homonyms © Kagan Publishing

Homonyms © Kagan Publishing

fair

need

Homonyms © Kagan Publishing

Homonyms © Kagan Publishing

Mix-N-Match: Language Arts
Kagan Publishing • 1 (800) 933-2667 • www.KaganOnline.com

Homonyms

stare

flee

fare

knead

Homonyms

1. there — their

2. wear — where

3. hear — here

4. right — write

5. eight — ate

6. bare — bear

7. knot — not

8. tail — tale

9. buy — bye

10. know — no

11. sea — see

12. pain — pane

13. tide — tied

14. toe — tow

15. hole — whole

16. night — knight

17. stair — stare

18. flea — flee

19. fair — fare

20. need — knead

Mix-N-Match: Language Arts
Kagan Publishing • 1 (800) 933-2667 • www.KaganOnline.com

Parts of Speech

Students practice parts of speech by matching a word with its correct part of speech.

Quizzing Questions

▶ **A Cards: Words**
- What part of speech am I?

▶ **B Cards: Parts of Speech**
- Name a noun, verb, adjective, or pronoun.

Parts of Speech

Write the part of speech next to each word below.

Parts of Speech
Noun, Verb, Adjective, Pronoun

1. Dog_____

2. Tall_____

3. Run_____

4. He_____

5. Pen _____

6. Dark _____

7. Clap _____

8. She _____

9. Mother _____

10. Pretty _____

11. Hop_____

12. They_____

13. Mall _____

14. Sad_____

15. Jump_____

16. We_____

17. House_____

18. Bright_____

19. Fly_____

20. It_____

Mix-N-Match: Language Arts
Kagan Publishing • 1 (800) 933-2667 • www.KaganOnline.com

Parts of Speech

Write four nouns, verbs, adjectives, and pronouns in the boxes below. Pair up with a partner and read one word. See if he or she can tell you what part of speech your word is. Take turns until you have shared your whole list.

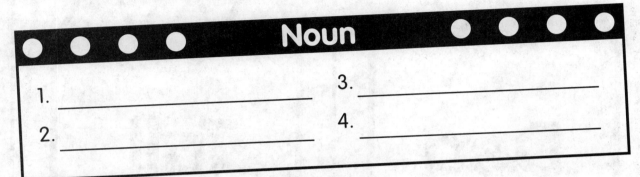

Noun

1. _____
2. _____
3. _____
4. _____

Verb

1. _____
2. _____
3. _____
4. _____

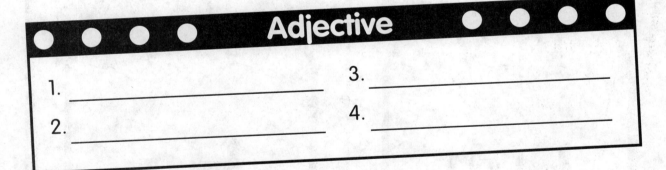

Adjective

1. _____
2. _____
3. _____
4. _____

Pronoun

1. _____
2. _____
3. _____
4. _____

Parts of Speech

Dog

Tall

Run

He

Parts of Speech © Kagan Publishing

Parts of Speech © Kagan Publishing

Parts of Speech © Kagan Publishing

Parts of Speech © Kagan Publishing

Parts of Speech

Pen

Parts of Speech © Kagan Publishing

Dark

Parts of Speech © Kagan Publishing

Clap

Parts of Speech © Kagan Publishing

She

Parts of Speech © Kagan Publishing

Mix-N-Match: Language Arts
Kagan Publishing • 1 (800) 933-2667 • www.KaganOnline.com

Parts of Speech

Noun

Parts of Speech © Kagan Publishing

Adjective

Parts of Speech © Kagan Publishing

Verb

Parts of Speech © Kagan Publishing

Pronoun

Parts of Speech © Kagan Publishing

Parts of Speech

Mix-N-Match: Language Arts
Kagan Publishing • 1 (800) 933-2667 • www.KaganOnline.com

Parts of Speech

Noun

Parts of Speech © Kagan Publishing

Adjective

Parts of Speech © Kagan Publishing

Verb

Parts of Speech © Kagan Publishing

Pronoun

Parts of Speech © Kagan Publishing

Parts of Speech

Mall

Parts of Speech © Kagan Publishing

Sad

Parts of Speech © Kagan Publishing

Jump

Parts of Speech © Kagan Publishing

We

Parts of Speech © Kagan Publishing

Mix-N-Match: Language Arts
Kagan Publishing • 1 (800) 933-2667 • www.KaganOnline.com

Parts of Speech

Noun

Parts of Speech © Kagan Publishing

Adjective

Parts of Speech © Kagan Publishing

Verb

Parts of Speech © Kagan Publishing

Pronoun

Parts of Speech © Kagan Publishing

Parts of Speech

Parts of Speech © Kagan Publishing

Parts of Speech © Kagan Publishing

Parts of Speech © Kagan Publishing

Parts of Speech © Kagan Publishing

Parts of Speech

Noun

Parts of Speech © Kagan Publishing

Adjective

Parts of Speech © Kagan Publishing

Verb

Parts of Speech © Kagan Publishing

Pronoun

Parts of Speech © Kagan Publishing

Parts of Speech

Nouns
- Dog
- Pen
- Mother
- Mall
- House

Verbs
- Run
- Clap
- Hop
- Jump
- Fly

Adjectives
- Tall
- Dark
- Pretty
- Sad
- Bright

Pronouns
- He
- She
- They
- We
- It

Mix-N-Match: Language Arts
Kagan Publishing • 1 (800) 933-2667 • www.KaganOnline.com

Prefixes

Students learn and practice prefixes by matching the prefix with its meaning.

Quizzing Questions

▶ **A Cards: Prefixes**
  • What do I mean?
  • Name a word that uses this prefix.
▶ **B Cards: Meanings**
  • What is my prefix?

Prefixes

Write the meaning of each prefix.

1. anti- _____

2. auto- _____

3. bene- _____

4. bi- _____

5. circu- _____

6. co- _____

7. equi- _____

8. inter- _____

9. intra- _____

10. mal- _____

11. mega- _____

12. multi- _____

13. neo- _____

14. non- _____

15. post- _____

16. pre- _____

17. pseudo- _____

18. sub- _____

19. tri- _____

20. uni- _____

unicycle

152

automobile

Prefixes

**Draw a line connecting
the prefix with its meaning.**

a. anti-

b. auto-

c. bene-

d. bi-

e. circu-

f. co-

g. equi-

h. inter-

i. intra-

j. mal-

k. mega-

l. multi-

m. neo-

n. non-

o. post-

p. pre-

q. pseudo-

r. sub-

s. tri-

t. uni-

1. among, between

2. under

3. two

4. together

5. within

6. around

7. bad

8. new

9. against

10. beneficial

11. after

12. large

13. equal

14. not

15. false

16. self

17. three

18. one

19. before

20. many, much

Prefixes

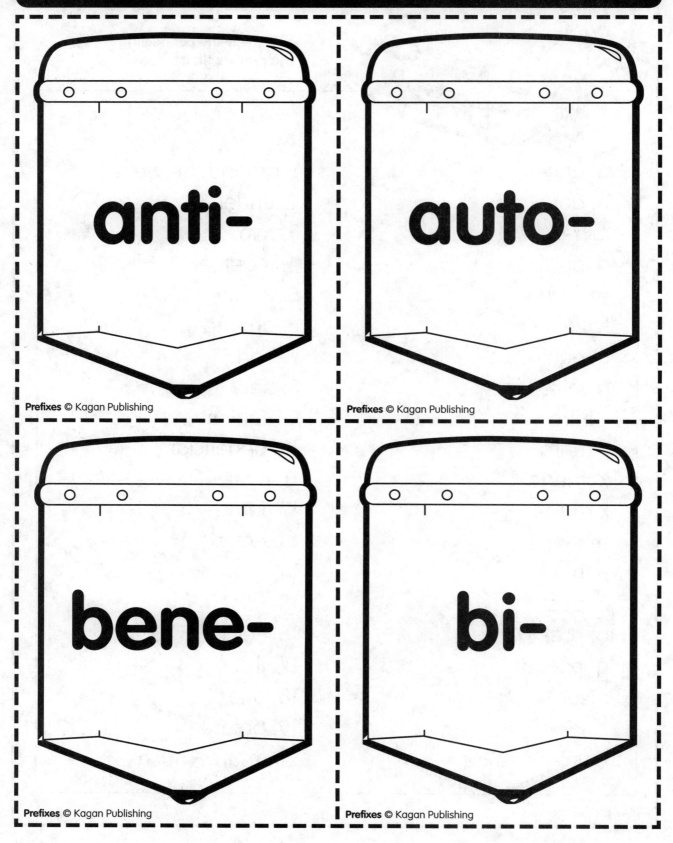

anti-

Prefixes © Kagan Publishing

auto-

Prefixes © Kagan Publishing

bene-

Prefixes © Kagan Publishing

bi-

Prefixes © Kagan Publishing

Mix-N-Match: Language Arts
Kagan Publishing • 1 (800) 933-2667 • www.KaganOnline.com

Prefixes

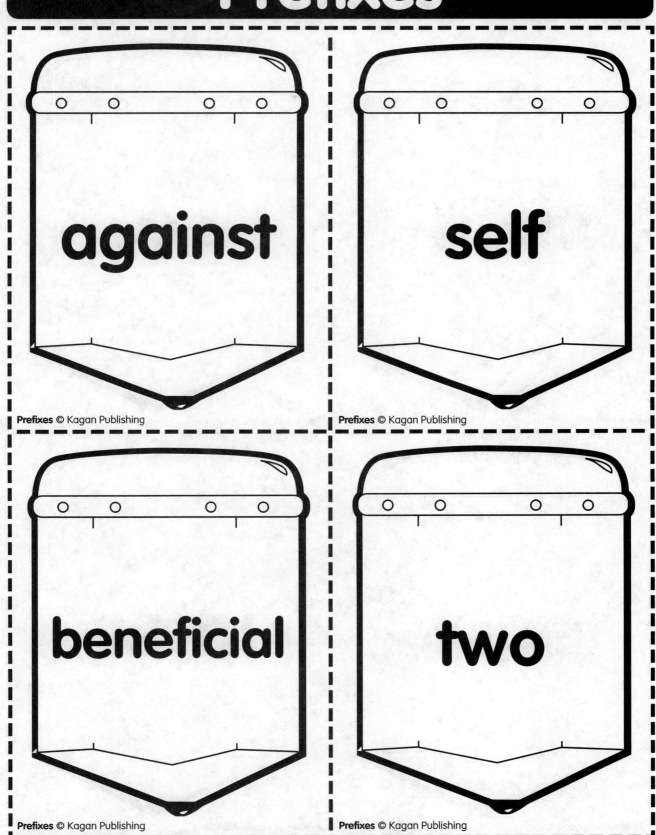

against

self

beneficial

two

Prefixes © Kagan Publishing

Prefixes © Kagan Publishing

Prefixes © Kagan Publishing

Prefixes © Kagan Publishing

Prefixes

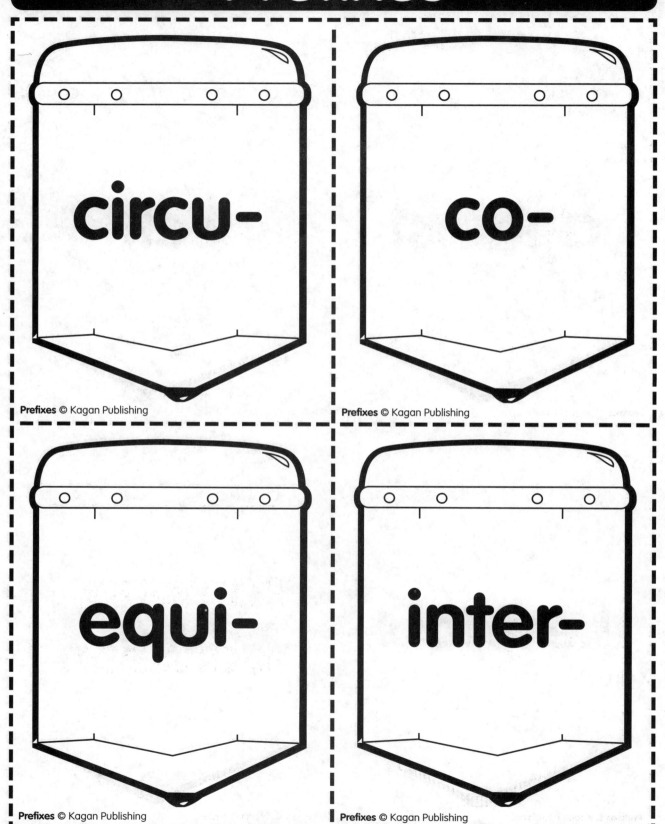

circu-

co-

equi-

inter-

Prefixes

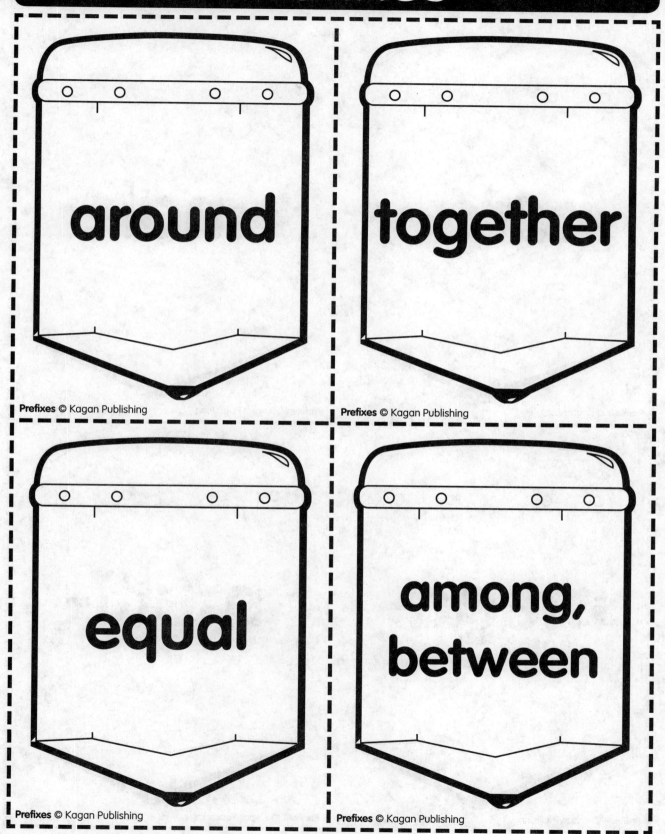

around

together

equal

among, between

Prefixes © Kagan Publishing

Prefixes © Kagan Publishing

Prefixes © Kagan Publishing

Prefixes © Kagan Publishing

Prefixes

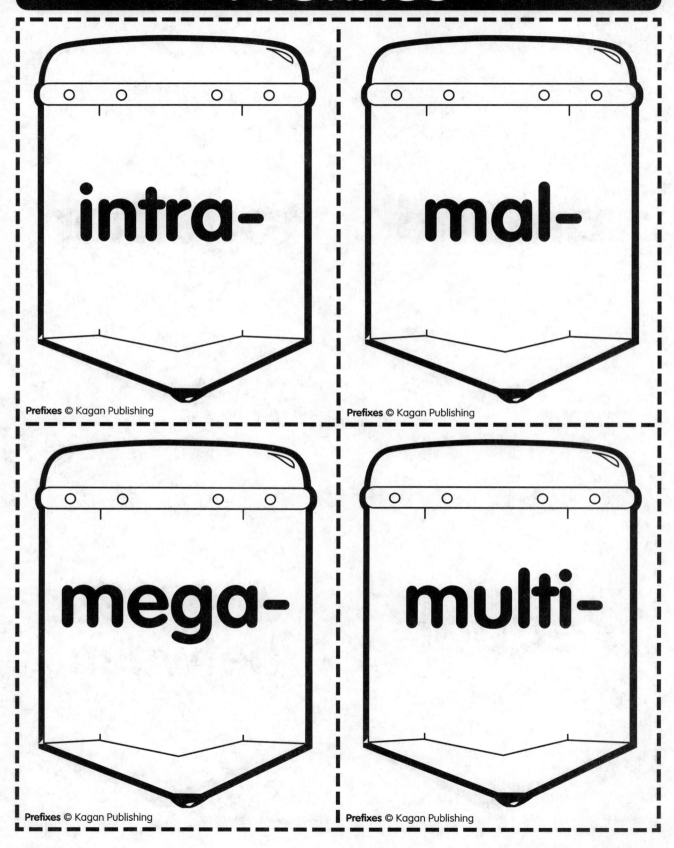

intra-

mal-

mega-

multi-

Mix-N-Match: Language Arts
Kagan Publishing • 1 (800) 933-2667 • www.KaganOnline.com

Prefixes

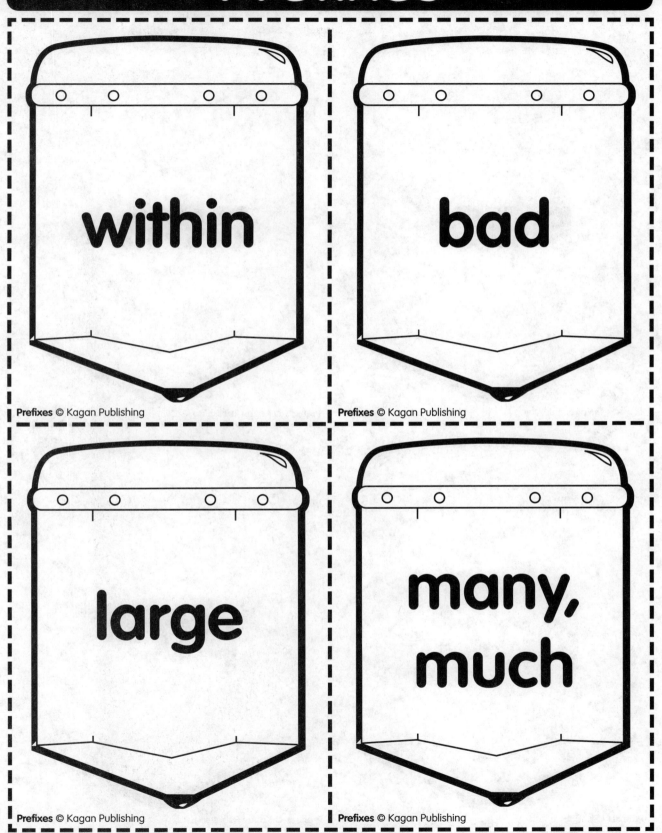

within

Prefixes © Kagan Publishing

bad

Prefixes © Kagan Publishing

large

Prefixes © Kagan Publishing

many,
much

Prefixes © Kagan Publishing

Prefixes

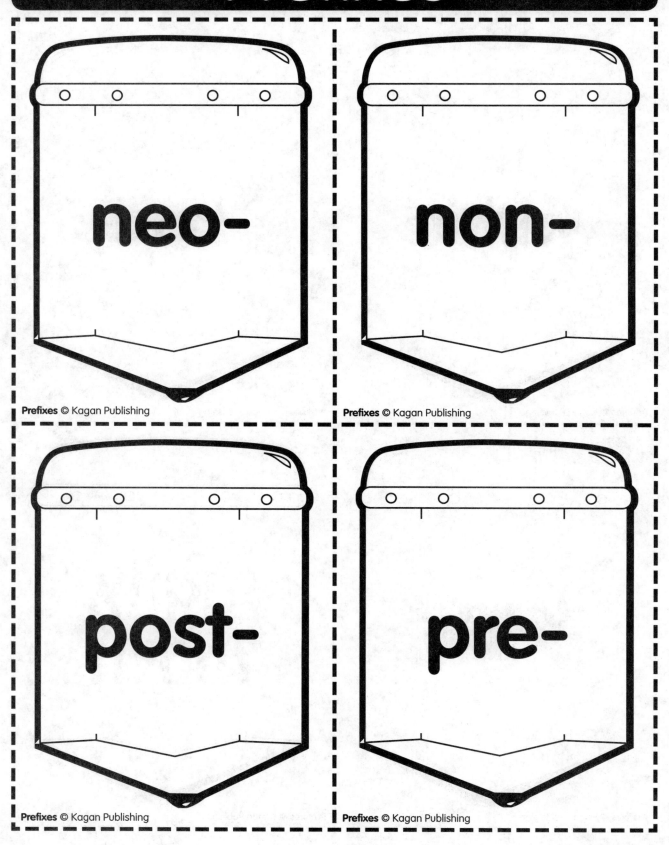

neo-

non-

post-

pre-

Prefixes © Kagan Publishing

Prefixes © Kagan Publishing

Prefixes © Kagan Publishing

Prefixes © Kagan Publishing

Mix-N-Match: Language Arts
Kagan Publishing • 1 (800) 933-2667 • www.KaganOnline.com

Prefixes

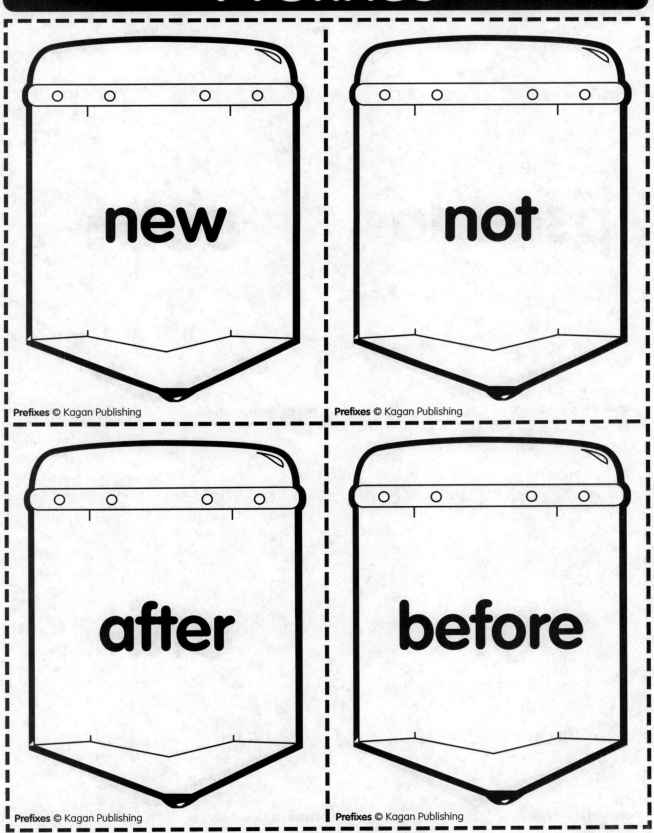

new

Prefixes © Kagan Publishing

not

Prefixes © Kagan Publishing

after

Prefixes © Kagan Publishing

before

Prefixes © Kagan Publishing

Prefixes

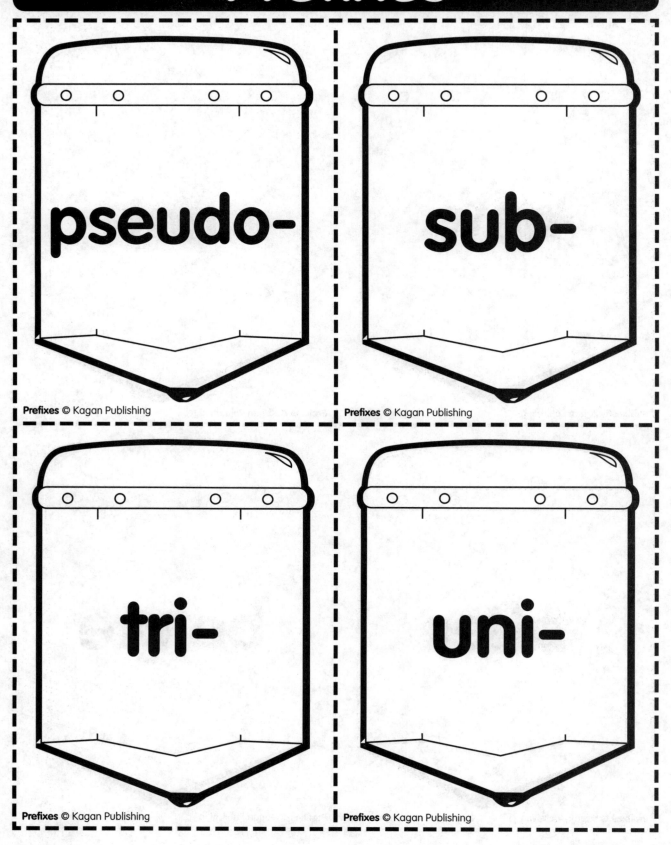

pseudo-

sub-

tri-

uni-

Prefixes © Kagan Publishing

Prefixes © Kagan Publishing

Prefixes © Kagan Publishing

Prefixes © Kagan Publishing

Mix-N-Match: Language Arts
Kagan Publishing • 1 (800) 933-2667 • www.KaganOnline.com

Prefixes

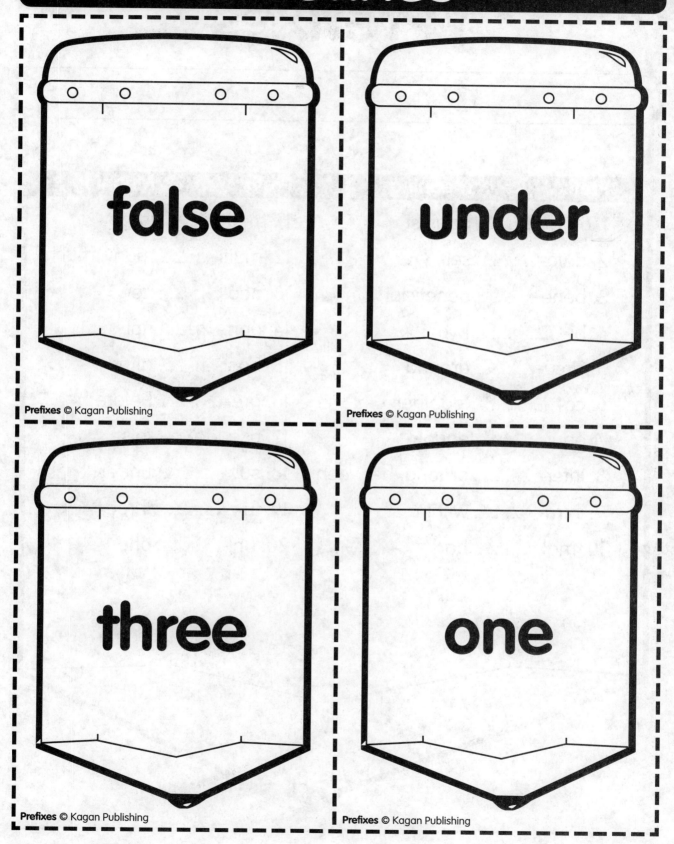

false

under

Prefixes © Kagan Publishing

Prefixes © Kagan Publishing

three

one

Prefixes © Kagan Publishing

Prefixes © Kagan Publishing

Prefixes

Prefix	Meaning	Prefix	Meaning
1. anti-	against	11. mega-	large
2. auto-	self	12. multi-	many, much
3. bene-	beneficial	13. neo-	new
4. bi-	two	14. non-	not
5. circu-	around	15. post-	after
6. co-	together	16. pre-	before
7. equi-	equal	17. pseudo-	false
8. inter-	among, between	18. sub-	under
9. intra-	within	19. tri-	three
10. mal-	bad	20. uni-	one

Mix-N-Match: Language Arts
Kagan Publishing • 1 (800) 933-2667 • www.KaganOnline.com

Synonyms

Students practice synonyms by matching up words with similar meanings.

Quizzing Questions

▶ **A Cards: Synonym 1**
  • What is a synonym for this word?
▶ **B Cards: Synonym 2**
  • What is a synonym for this word?

Synonyms

Draw a line connecting the synonyms in Columns 1 and 2.

Column 1	Column 2
like	depart
leave	unhappy
scared	pal
sad	sofa
couch	supper
friend	afraid
recall	enjoy
save	evening
night	remember
dinner	keep

syn • o • nym (n.) – a word having the same or nearly the same meaning as another word.

Mix-N-Match: Language Arts
Kagan Publishing • 1 (800) 933-2667 • www.KaganOnline.com

Synonyms

Draw a line connecting the synonyms in Columns 1 and 2.

Column 1	Column 2
cheerful	cheap
angry	talk
create	gift
inexpensive	fast
chat	mad
car	cry
quick	happy
weep	big
large	automobile
present	make

syn • o • nym (n.) – a word having the same or nearly the same meaning as another word.

Synonyms

like

leave

scared

sad

Synonyms

enjoy

depart

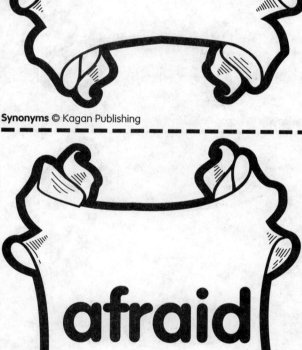

afraid

unhappy

Synonyms

couch

friend

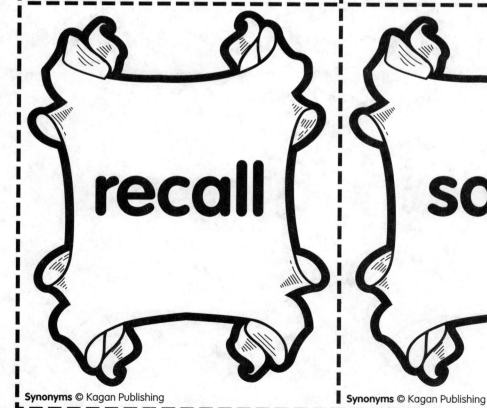

recall

save

Synonyms

sofa

pal

remember

keep

Synonyms

night

dinner

happy

mad

Synonyms

evening

supper

cheerful

angry

Synonyms © Kagan Publishing

Synonyms

make

cheap

talk

automobile

Mix-N-Match: Language Arts
Kagan Publishing • 1 (800) 933-2667 • www.KaganOnline.com

Synonyms

create

Synonyms © Kagan Publishing

inexpensive

Synonyms © Kagan Publishing

chat

Synonyms © Kagan Publishing

car

Synonyms © Kagan Publishing

Synonyms

fast

cry

big

gift

Synonyms

quick

weep

large

present

Synonyms

1. like.............................enjoy
2. leave ....depart
3. scared ....afraid
4. sad ....unhappy
5. couch ....sofa
6. friend........................pal
7. recall.........................remember
8. save..........................keep
9. night ....evening
10. dinner ....supper
11. happy ....cheerful
12. mad ....angry
13. make ....create
14. cheap......................inexpensive
15. talk ....chat
16. automobile ....car
17. fast ....quick
18. cry ....weep
19. big...........................large
20. gift ....present

Mix-N-Match: Language Arts
Kagan Publishing • 1 (800) 933-2667 • www.KaganOnline.com

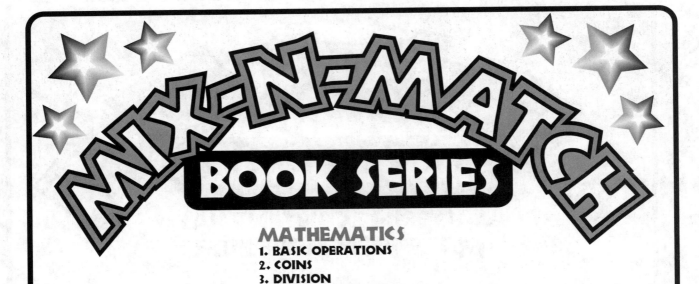

MIX-N-MATCH BOOK SERIES

MATHEMATICS
1. BASIC OPERATIONS
2. COINS
3. DIVISION
4. EQUIVALENT FRACTIONS
5. FRACTIONS AND PERCENTS
6. GRAPHING ORDERED PAIRS
7. MEASUREMENT CONVERSIONS
8. MULTIPLICATION
9. PLACE VALUE
10. READING TIME
11. ROMAN NUMERALS
12. SUBTRACTION

LANGUAGE ARTS
1. ABBREVIATIONS
2. ANTONYMS
3. CLASSIFYING NOUNS
4. COMPOUND WORDS
5. CONTRACTIONS
6. DICTIONARY GUIDE WORDS
7. DOUBLE LETTER SPELLING WORDS
8. FACT OR OPINION
9. HOMONYMS
10. PARTS OF SPEECH
11. PREFIXES
12. SYNONYMS

LOOK WHAT'S INSIDE!

SOCIAL STUDIES
1. FAMOUS AMERICANS
2. FAMOUS PLACES
3. FIRE SAFETY
4. GEOGRAPHY VOCABULARY
5. HISTORICAL EVENTS
6. HOLIDAYS
7. INVENTIONS
8. LANDFORMS
9. STATE GEOGRAPHY
10. STATES AND CAPITALS
11. THE BILL OF RIGHTS
12. WORLD GEOGRAPHY

PRIMARY
1. ADDITION
2. ANIMALS
3. BEGINNING CONSONANTS AND VOWELS
4. COMMUNITY HELPERS
5. FOOD
6. LESS THAN, GREATER THAN
7. LETTERS
8. NUMBERS AND DOTS
9. ORDINAL NUMBERS
10. SHAPES
11. THE MISSING LETTER
12. TRANSPORTATION

SCIENCE
1. ANIMAL ADULT AND BABY NAMES
2. ANIMAL CLASSIFICATION
3. BODY PARTS
4. BUGS AND INSECTS
5. CELL ANATOMY
6. EXPLORING SPACE VOCABULARY
7. HUMAN BODY FUN FACTS
8. HUMAN BODY SYSTEMS
9. MATTER AND ENERGY VOCABULARY
10. OCEAN LIFE
11. THE FOOD PYRAMID
12. WEATHER VOCABULARY

CALL FOR FREE CATALOGS! OR VISIT US ONLINE!

1 (800) 933-2667 Kagan WWW.KAGANONLINE.COM

Made in the USA
Coppell, TX
24 June 2023